It's "TIME" to Make *More* Money with Watch Repairs

The Fine Art of Making Watch Repairs Profitable for YOU!

NOW- Includes *"Keys to Successful Selling"*
and
"Start Your Own PictureWatch Business"!

by Dan & Sheila Gendron

www.watchfix.com www.watchrepairseminars.com
www.watchrepairvideos.com www.watchrepairbooks.com

ISBN 0-9728649-6-2
Copyright © 2004 by Dan Gendron Horology

Printed in the U.S.A.

Published by:
Dan Gendron Horology
Timberon NM 88350
888-750-3330
Cover Design by Sheila Gendron

www.watchfix.com   www.watchrepairseminars.com
www.watchrepairvideos.com www.watchrepairbooks.com

Table of Contents

This book is dedicated to my family:

To my wife, Sheila, without whose long hours of loving patience this book would not have become a reality.

To my father, Henri Louis Gendron, and my mother, Doris Gendron, who taught me the trade -- and much more.

To my brothers, Mark and Gordon Gendron, whose experiences, combined with mine, make up the fabric of this book.

Dan's Grandfather circa 1900

www.watchfix.com   www.watchrepairseminars.com
www.watchrepairvideos.com   www.watchrepairbooks.com

Dan & brother on Dad's knee circa 1960

Dan's Grandfather circa 1900

Dan's Grandfather's store, Gendron's Jewelry circa 1935

5

Introduction

I have heard it said that there are three types of people in the world, as it relates to sensual experiences – the auditory, the tactile and the visual. I, however, am inspired by the olfactory. I become nostalgic remembering the smells of this trade. In the case of my father's shop in the finished basement of our suburban Rhode Island home, those smells included watch cleaning solution, naptha, mobus (whale oil), and Winston cigarettes. To this day, whenever I have the privilege of cleaning out the estate of a deceased watchmaker, it's the smells that get me every time. The smells bring to mind the many times that I would hear my mother say things like, "Louie, was that an AS970 balance staff or an AS976?" Or my father saying, "Doris, call Chasan's and order an Omega 484 fourth wheel." This was the world in which I grew up.

I get asked quite a bit by people in the jewelry trade why I remained in this business during the lean times. It can be very hard to make someone understand that you do something simply because you love it. The real purpose of

www.watchfix.com   www.watchrepairseminars.com
www.watchrepairvideos.com www.watchrepairbooks.com

this book, over and above helping you make the watch repairs that you deal with profitable, is to share that love with you in order to help you learn to love it too.

-- Dan Gendron CMH

www.watchfix.com   www.watchrepairseminars.com
www.watchrepairvideos.com   www.watchrepairbooks.com

Chapter 1
Interfacing with the Customer

www.watchfix.com   www.watchrepairseminars.com
www.watchrepairvideos.com www.watchrepairbooks.com

SETTING CUSTOMER EXPECTATIONS

Nearly every jeweler in the country has a "good reason" to hate watches. Often, the reason to hate watches is because of an irate customer who caused a scene in their store.

If a jeweler has had a bad experience with a customer while making a diamond sale, it certainly wouldn't make sense for him to abandon diamond sales because of it, but this is exactly what many jewelers do when it comes to watch sales and repairs.

The solution is to set reasonable expectations for the customer and ourselves. This will prevent bad feelings on both sides of the counter.

We, as retailers, need to educate our customers on what to expect. Often it is we who give the customer unrealistic expectations. We do this many times because the person that taught us the trade treated his customers this way. I remember seeing an old-time jeweler making promises that he knew he could not keep. How many times has the

www.watchfix.com   www.watchrepairseminars.com
www.watchrepairvideos.com www.watchrepairbooks.com

customer told you when he would be back to pick up a repaired watch, and you failed to stop him, and then tried to meet his deadline? Never tell a customer anything that you cannot be virtually 100 percent sure you can fulfill.

We have many jewelers call us and tell us that their customer expected a watch back by a certain date. This shows that the sales clerk at the counter did not take that first opportunity to set the customer's expectations. This is a recipe for a dissatisfied customer. The retail watch repair customer enters your store with no clearly defined expectations, or completely unrealistic ones. The watch repair business is unpredictable at best. Be sure to promise only what you can deliver. What works best is to under promise and over deliver. For example if most of the time you can deliver a certain type of repair in 2 weeks, promise it in 3 weeks. If we make our promises to our customers in this fashion, most of the time we will surprise the customer by being early and not late.

Would you expect to be able to go into a dry cleaner's and tell the clerk when you wanted your suit back, what you would pay for it, and how you expected it to look when you came back? When you drop something off at the dry cleaner, first they will tell you which spots they will get out and which ones they won't. Next they will ask "Did you want it express service, or would 3-4 days later be OK?" (Express service costs more than the 3-4 day service.) Actually, this is an excellent closing question. (That is defined as any question you ask that, when the customer answers in the affirmative, it means they have bought.) This type of closing question is called the "Alternate Choice" close. It is called this because it does ask the buying question, but offers the customer more than one choice.

The dry cleaner has immediately set the customer's expectation. That is our job as well. We want to make money for the company we own or work for, and setting customer expectations is the key. This is always our job, not the customer's. I know jewelers who hand the customer a blank repair envelope and have them fill it out. Unfortunately, some customers fill out repair envelopes better than some jewelers would have .

Lawyers have this to say about the litigious public: "Anything not stated is certain to become a problem." And for our purposes, any customer expectation not addressed is certain to become a problem.

When the customer drops off a watch for repair, if we fail to clearly define what the customer can expect, everything that can go wrong will go wrong. It will be there a day late. It won't have a new watchband on it. It won't have the dial refinished. And his great-grandfather's 150-year-old pocket watch won't be as accurate as a modern watch.

How many times has the customer approached you in the store with a familiar watch in his hands, and before they open their mouth, you know why they are there? We are responsible for everything our customers expect. If we set no expectations, the customer will, invariably, expect that which is impossible.

First, we must adjust the customer's expectation of when his watch will be ready to our repair schedule. We must do this before the customer asks when he can expect to have it back. When you beat the customer to the punch on this question, almost nothing you say will be a problem. But if you wait for him to ask, any time you give him will not be soon enough.

Some of the best jewelry stores I have been in have a one-day-per-sheet calendar or a sign beside the counter that reads, "Watch repairs taken in today will be ready (future date)." The customer's expectations are set immediately and the question doesn't come up. That is not to say that you shouldn't tell the customer directly as well.

✓ Take Action NOW!

Let's say today's date is June 8th and the calendar says that watch repairs left today will be ready on June 26th. This looks better to the customer than saying the watch will be done "in about two weeks." Two weeks seems much longer than June 26th does. In general, avoid vague terms such as, "in about a week", "in a couple of weeks," or such.

By giving a specific finish date, there is no longer confusion. The time for the repair becomes concrete and achievable. It makes no difference if the finish date is one

www.watchfix.com   www.watchrepairseminars.com
www.watchrepairvideos.com   www.watchrepairbooks.com

month in the future, as long as the date is clearly defined. Take the time to do this and virtually all of your customers' expectations on when they can expect their watch back will be met.

Take the time to investigate the type of watch your customer has. When they drop off a watch for a battery, a tune-up, a service, take time to point out to them what the reasonable expectations are for the water resistance capabilities of their watch. This eliminates the possibility of someone taking a plain, level one water resist Pulsar and jumping in the hot tub wearing it, and then come back to you saying that their watch now leaks.

In your addendum are the water resistance charts for all watches. Make copies of them for your customers. They let your customers know what they can expect from their watch and what they can expect from your maintenance and repair work.

We also must let the customer know what to expect from the timing performance of a specific watch. For example, if your customer has a 100-year-old pocket watch with 7 or 15 jewels, ideally it is reasonable that the watch be expected keep time to within 30-60 seconds a day.

What other factors may be involved in how a watch performs?

When repairing a watch this old, it is important to ask the customer what he plans on doing with this watch. Many times the customer will state that he will be giving this pocket watch to his grandson, who is a laborer on a construction site.

Not a good idea. But you wouldn't know if you didn't ask. In this case, as it is with all watches made before the WWII, they lack an unbreakable balance staff or "Incablock". Suffice it to say we need to ask a lot of questions so that we can set the reasonable expectations.

There are many people who drop their watch off for repair and expect that when they receive it back the crystal will be new, the band will be new and the case will look "as new."

www.watchfix.com   www.watchrepairseminars.com
www.watchrepairvideos.com www.watchrepairbooks.com

We need to put ourselves in the state of mind that the customer is in when he drops off the repair.

We have just told him how much the repair will cost and he will assume that, for that price, everything will look at least better than when he brought it in, whether he asked for it or not. Here, again, it is our job to set the customer's expectations. We do this by inspecting the watch item by item, with the customer's participation (See Preliminary Estimates).

I have a great watch repair trade account who sends vintage watches to be repaired. I know without ever having to speak to him that he expects a new band, new spring bars, new crystal, dial refinish, crown replaced and case polished, at minimum.

He is someone who understands the art of presentation. He has let me know that when he delivers a watch to a customer, the first thing he notices is that their eyes light up at the sight of their old, worn out watch, which looks new and beautiful again.

www.watchfix.com   www.watchrepairseminars.com
www.watchrepairvideos.com www.watchrepairbooks.com

He had set the customer's expectations at the point of sale, and they weren't disappointed when they came to pick it up. It's so easy for a customer to see something, such as a band, crystal, or crown that could have been repaired, and at the point of presentation immediately feel that he was overcharged.

We have a responsibility to our customers to do everything we know how to do to give them a product that they, and we, can be proud of. We need to stop concerning ourselves with how much of our customers' money we spend (that is their decision), and concentrate on the presentation of the end product.

How many good jewelers would replace the tips on a ring where the shank had worn thin? How many good jewelers would solder a chain and polish it in only one spot? You wouldn't dare do that, would you? So why do half the job with watches?

When the customer picks up his watch, and it sparkles and looks new and clean, any misgivings the customer may have

www.watchfix.com   www.watchrepairseminars.com
www.watchrepairvideos.com   www.watchrepairbooks.com

had about spending the money to have it "reconditioned" fall by the wayside quickly. Conversely, anything we fail to remedy causes the customer to feel that they did not get their money's worth.

Here is a simple exercise for you. If the most important person on earth came into your store to have a watch repaired, what would you make sure to do for that customer?

✓ *Make Sure You Offer The Best Service!*
This Eliminates the Competition. It's easy to stand out,
because so few really try to please the customer.

Well, every customer that comes in to your store is the most important person on earth. If you treat them with such consideration, your customers will sense it and appreciate it. Yes, there will be those who will feel it is too much money to spend. But we have those types of customers in jewelry circumstances, where we do not compromise and we should not compromise with watch repair, either. Treat all watch repairs as though you, personally, had to deliver them to the most important person on earth, bearing in mind that your prestige and your name goes with it.

✓ *Treat Your Repair Customers As Well As You Treat Your Merchandise Customers and They Will Become Them*

I can tell you from personal experience as well as the hundreds of students we have taught that we have reconditioned watches for people who have related to us how their friends had asked them where they bought the "new" watch, or how much the "new" watch cost. And they could tell those friends with pride that they just had their old watch reconditioned.

Remember it's your job to set your customers' expectations. Set them realistically. But set them *high enough* to meet your own standards.

TAKING IN A WATCH FOR REPAIR

A simple question… when you take in a .75 ct. diamond ring in a 14 karat mounting or a 2 ct. diamond ring in an 18 karat mounting to repair a prong and re-shank it, do you write the description as "diamond ring – fix"? Or are you meticulous in your description of the style of mounting, carat weight of the stone, type of metal, etc.? I can't tell you how many times we have received a job envelope with a two-tone Rolex inside described only as "Watch – fix"!

Far too many jewelry storeowners have unnecessarily had to "bite the bullet" on a watch repair expense, or worse due to a lack of proper take-in of the watch. A little time spent on what may seem to be trivial information can save you a world of headaches.

The first thing to do is get a repair envelope and begin to fill it out, even if the customer seems only to be "investigating" a repair. This is called the "Order Blank" close. (This close actually uses the Assumptive close (because you are already filling out the form) and the customer is brought along in the

www.watchfix.com   www.watchrepairseminars.com
www.watchrepairvideos.com www.watchrepairbooks.com

process by our questions. Fill in the personal information (name, address, and phone).) Even if the customer decides not to leave the watch, you have added a name to your valuable customer mailing list. Then take the information down about the watch.

The Cardinal Rule is: USE YOUR LOUPE! Besides enabling you to see the watch correctly, something very powerful goes on in the customer's mind when you use your loupe, because all retail sales begin in the eyes of the customer. As the customer sees you closely inspect their watch and sees the things that you list as wrong with the watch the process becomes genuine. But when we give it a cursory look, they doubt your veracity. *"People believe what they see, not what they hear!"* Talk less and show more!

1. Gent's or Ladies'?

2. Brand - USE YOUR LOUPE! Don't assume that a watch brand starting with "C" and ending with "R" is a Cartier. When you hand the customer back their "Carter" they

just might demand the "Cartier" they claim you checked in!

3. Yellow, White, Two-Tone? - NEVER "GOLD" OR "SILVER"! Even a case marked "14 KT" may not necessarily mean solid gold. The color of the watch is determined by the case, which may not always match the band.

4. Are there stones on the watch, band or dial? If so, describe them as "X" color stones. Even diamonds that you may verify with a diamond tester should be described as "White Stones," not diamonds. Check to see if any of the stones are missing and mark that. Also check to see if any of the stones are loose and mark that.

www.watchfix.com   www.watchrepairseminars.com
www.watchrepairvideos.com   www.watchrepairbooks.com

PRELIMINARY ESTIMATE:

One thing that we must remember is that our customers come into a jewelry store in a visual mode! By this I mean that they are there to SEE, not be told. *Customers believe what they see and NOT WHAT THEY HEAR!* To be congruent with this frame of mind we must be *showing* the customer the shortcomings of their watch. We accomplish this by using the preliminary estimate.

Having your watch repairperson do all of your estimates will lose you time, money and prestige. As a watch professional, your clients expect you to have some idea of what is wrong with their watch. This checklist will guide you through a preliminary estimate that you can do with the customer still at the counter, and have the customer understand and approve repair charges there and then, which is the goal of accepting a watch repair.

Of course, there are times and watches that *will* require your watch repairperson to give you a more detailed estimate, but these can be kept to a minimum. While performing the preliminary estimate, remember that the ultimate result of this transaction is to return to your customer a completely refurbished watch that they can leave the store with proudly, knowing that you have been the retailer who has given them outstanding, professional service.

Familiarize yourself with your repairperson's price list. Determine what markup you will add. When preparing a preliminary estimate, note each item needed on the repair envelope or job ticket, along with the corresponding charge.

After you have taken the customers information and basic description of the watch (brand, gents or ladies, color, any stones and what color), first determine whether the watch is or is not running. In the case in which you find that the watch is not running, be especially sure to state that to the customer. This will prevent a customer saying, "My watch was running until you touched it!"

If the watch is mechanical and running fast, slow, or not at all, the very least that watch will need is a service (overhaul). Mark that on the envelope along with the price.

www.watchfix.com   www.watchrepairseminars.com
www.watchrepairvideos.com   www.watchrepairbooks.com

In most cases, for the price of replacing an average quartz movement, any problem with a quartz watch that can't be remedied by changing the battery can be remedied by changing the movement.

Next, try winding the watch. Is it difficult, indicating rust? Does the stem come out in your hand? Is the crown worn or missing? If yes, mark and price a stem and/or crown and/or winding parts on the repair envelope.

Look closely at the dial. Is it discolored? Are there markers missing or loose under the crystal? Are there scratches on the dial? Is it peeling? If the answer to any of these is yes, mark the envelope for a dial refinish and price the repair accordingly. It is also possible to have a dial customized with a company logo, personal name, or other customization, even a Picture Watch, (see section on Picture Watches), or check with your watchmaker for possibilities.

Is the crystal broken, chipped, cracked or missing? Are there scuffs on the crystal that can not simply be polished out? If yes, mark the envelope for a new crystal and, again, price it accordingly.

Whether the band is metal or leather, determine if it is worn out or showing brass. Envision how that band will look if the case, crystal and crown are shiny and new and the band is not. Direct the customer to the band display and have him or her pick out a new one.

If the case is badly worn, showing brass or gouged, there is often no remedy for this, but make a notation of this condition anyway, for your own protection.

Go over each of the above items individually with your customer, and tell them the price you have calculated for the repair. Now, this is very important:

DO NOT APOLOGIZE FOR THE PRICE OF THE REPAIR, AND REMEMBER TO SMILE WHEN GIVING THEM THE PRICE!

Your service is a valuable one, one that cannot even be found in many retail jewelry establishments. Typically only 1 in 20 retail jewelers perform watch repairs on watches they do not sell. The truth is customers choose to have their watch repaired for one of several reasons, however, the most common reason is that the watch means something to them greater than the material value of the piece. Most often, it will have been a gift. You need to know that there are only two types of retail jewelry store customers: they are P customers and T customers. P customers shop price and T customers shop for someone they can trust. P customers typically shop discounters and the "–"Mart stores. T customers only shop at traditional jewelry stores, because these are the people that they trust. If you doubt it, consider this; would someone have price on their mind when the need to have their wedding bands that they have worn for 30 years repaired, or when having grand-dad's pocketwatch repaired. The answer is the only thing on their mind is TRUST, not PRICE!

Nearly 80% of all watches on people's wrists were gifts. This removes the cost consideration from the equation in many cases. We need to be careful to never make the customer feel that his or her watch isn't worth repairing. Sometimes that will be the case, however, we need to first price the repair then gauge the customer's response to that price before offering other alternatives such as a new watch.

✓ *Don't make the customer feel funny about paying a fair price for good service.*

Additionally, let them know that if the watchmaker finds any other problems once inside the watch, that you will notify the customer before proceeding with any work. The watch may require a mainspring, a balance staff, or another part or service that cannot be determined without actually opening the watch. Mark the envelope *"If More, Call"* so that your watchmaker knows that you want an estimate if you have missed something.

After all this explanation, there is a simpler way to handle estimates. ASSUME FULL SERVICE, that is, when any watch is sent from your store to your watch repair trade shop or your in house repairperson, instruct them to give the watch *FULL SERVICE*.

www.watchfix.com   www.watchrepairseminars.com
www.watchrepairvideos.com www.watchrepairbooks.com

Often this will automatically include a new crown, new crystal, installation of the band that the customer has picked out, as well as the overhaul of the mechanics (or in the case of quartz, a new movement) of the watch.

Let your customer know, and be proud of the fact, that on all watches that you service you provide *complete* service, so that the entire watch comes back to the customer in a condition that will be virtually worry-free and a piece that he can be proud to wear. Communicate to your watchmaker that this is what you want on all your repairs.

The next step in the take-in process is…

GET THEIR MONEY!

Yes, I said, *"Get their money."* This is not as frightening as it may sound. A simple, assumptive close is generally the best way to accomplish this:

First, SMILE. The best way I know of to keep the customer completely at ease is to smile frequently, broadly, and sincerely. Your customers will give you money much more easily when you smile. The truth is that many times we are so afraid to tell the customers the price that we forget the most important part, SMILE! "Would you like to pay for that with a check, cash, or credit card?" (Alternate Choice Close.)

Unless you have decided to be a charitable organization, you do expect to be paid for your services, don't you? Don't assume that the customer will hate you for asking for payment. Actually, your request for payment will let the customer know that you are confident in your ability to perform this service.

If getting full payment at the time of take in is too far beyond your comfort zone, get at least a partial payment at the time of take-in. Even if the watch needs to be completely estimated by your watchmaker, charge a nominal fee for the estimate. This accomplishes two things. First of all, if the customer declines the estimate, you have at least covered your shipping charges if any and if nothing else you made a modest profit for handling the watch. Secondly, it is a measure of their sincerity in wanting the watch repaired. Sometimes a customer will give an OK to the repair if we do not ask for money, even though they have no intention of ever returning to pick up the watch. But when we ask for money -- whether it's a full payment or deposit -- the truth comes out. Too many jewelers have thousands of dollars of un-claimed repairs in their safe that not one dollar has ever been paid and most likely never will be.

Comebacks

Watches are delicate instruments. It is the "nature of the beast" that you will experience some amount of comebacks, that is, a watch that has recently been repaired needing to be re-repaired. *Don't overreact*, especially in front of the customer. Don't always assume your watchmaker is at fault, for as many times as not, it will be a case of the customer not knowing how to treat or properly use their watch. Take it in stride, assuring the customer that you will have any problem corrected for them, and take the responsibility to ensure that your customer knows everything he or she should to prevent an unnecessary trip back to the repair shop. Take the time to check the watch yourself. Sometimes the customer will not really have a problem. If the customer says the watch stops, check it yourself. All too often there is no real problem, and if we send the watch out to the repair shop (especially if we must ship the watch to a off location trade shop) without knowing for sure, we may waste postage, time, and trouble. Too many times the customers imagined problem is just that -- *IMAGINED*! Now, don't *assume* that the customer is wrong, just take the time to know!

.

www.watchfix.com   www.watchrepairseminars.com
www.watchrepairvideos.com www.watchrepairbooks.com

Repair Take-In Checklist:

Customer Name
Address
Phone (Work & Home)

Your Job #_____
Watch Description:
 Men's   Ladies'

Yellow   White   T/T   Other

Brand
Quartz or Mechanical?
Stones (Y/N)   Color of Stones

Water Resistance Level

Insurance Value $
Is the item appraised?
Customer Acknowledgment (initial)_____

Preliminary Estimate:

Problem Description:

Is the Watch Running?	**Price $:**
Stem/Crown Broken or Missing?	**Price $:**
Condition of Crystal?	**Price $:**
Condition of Dial?	**Price $:**
Condition of Case?	**Price $:**
Condition of Band?	**Price $:**

Total Preliminary Estimate: $

Is Watchmaker's Estimate Required:
Cost for Estimate: $

WATER RESISTANCE

There is scarcely any subject I know of about which there is more confusion to retailers and clients alike than the term "Water Resistant" as regards watches. In the 1950s and the early 1960s, the Federal Trade Commission (FTC) had no standards for what constituted a waterproof watch.

In that type of environment, we had Timex claiming to be waterproof, as well as Rolex. This caused a rash of complaints, so the FTC hastily put together some standards, which were so ambiguous as to cause more confusion than not having any. However, they did ban the use of the term "WaterPROOF" altogether.

Then in the early 1970s the FTC adopted the rules that are currently in use today. They are not perfect, but they are better than anything we have had in the past. On the following pages are the FTC standard definitions of the four different "Water Resistance" standards in use today.

www.watchfix.com   www.watchrepairseminars.com
www.watchrepairvideos.com www.watchrepairbooks.com

First of all, only watches that are stamped "water resistant" on the back of the case, can be called water-resistant at all. Furthermore, the depth notation is only valid if also marked on the case back. A number on the dial, such as a "Sports 100" is not an indication of the water resistance, unless it specifically says "meters" along with the number.

www.watchfix.com   www.watchrepairseminars.com
www.watchrepairvideos.com www.watchrepairbooks.com

WATER RESISTANCE GRADE DEFINITIONS

GENERAL WATER RESISTANCE: A watch that on the case back is stamped "Water Resistant" and nothing else (no number).

This watch is NOT water resistant in the following cases:
- professional deep water diving;
- recreational SCUBA diving;
- bathing,
- swimming,
- snorkeling,
- hot-tubbing.

It does have sufficient water-resistant characteristics for:
- being out in the rain
- washing one's hands.

HIGH GRADE WATER RESISTANCE: The case back will be marked "Water Resistant 50m"(eters).

This watch is NOT water resistant in the following cases:
- professional deep water diving;
- recreational SCUBA diving;
- hot-tubbing, bathing.

It is water resistant for
- swimming,
- snorkeling,
- being out in the rain
- washing one's hands.

www.watchfix.com   www.watchrepairseminars.com
www.watchrepairvideos.com www.watchrepairbooks.com

DIVERS WATCH: The case back will be marked "Water Resistant 100m"(eters).

This watch is NOT water resistant in the following cases:
- professional deep water diving.

It is water resistant for
- recreational SCUBA diving;
- hot-tubbing,
- bathing;
- swimming;
- snorkeling;
- being out in the rain
- washing one's hands.

PROFESSIONAL DIVERS WATCH: The case back will be marked "Water Resistant 300m"(eters) and up.

This watch* is water resistant for
- professional deep water diving;
- recreational SCUBA diving;
- hot-tubbing, bathing;
- swimming;
- snorkeling;
- being out in the rain
- washing one's hands.

*NOTE: Of the major watch brands, I know of only Rolex? [1] Sea-Dweller and Citizen ProMaster Divers' watches to be at this level of water resistance.

TAKING ACTION - CHAPTER 1

✓ Take time to use the Repair Take-In Checklist for ALL repairs. (This is also known as an "Order Blank Close".)

✓ Have your retail price list available at the front counter.

✓ Ensure that all repairs you handle (watch and jewelry) are done to the highest level of proficiency. Include all areas that you can see that are in need of improvement, e.g., crystal, dial, band, crown, etc. You determine what repairs are necessary, not the customer.

✓ Set customers' expectations as to when their watch repairs will be completed before the customer asks.

✓ Have the Water Resistance definitions chart available at the front counter.

✓ Determine the Water Resistance level of all watches you handle and make sure the customer is aware of the water resistance capabilities of his/her watch.

www.watchfix.com   www.watchrepairseminars.com
www.watchrepairvideos.com   www.watchrepairbooks.com

✓ Do not apologize for the price of the repair. Practice giving the customer the price with a smile on your face. Know that you are offering truly unique service.

✓ Practice assumptive, alternate-choice closes when you give the customer the price for the repair, e.g., "Would you like to pay for that with a check, cash, or credit card?"

✓ Treat every customer you meet as if he or she was the most important person on earth – they are.

TAKE ACTION NOW!

Chapter 2
Pricing the Sale and Selling the Price

www.watchfix.com   www.watchrepairseminars.com
www.watchrepairvideos.com www.watchrepairbooks.com

PRICING WATCH REPAIRS

There are as many different philosophies on how to price a repair, as there are jewelers who price them. But it is not how low the price of a repair is that will bring the right customers in. That is not the type of customer who will enable you to become more profitable.

The public has a genuine yearning for high quality service. The public is desperately seeking business professionals and salespersons they can truly believe in. The quality customers come to your store because you offer quality service. You want to stand apart from what the "crowd" of jewelers does, don't you?

The best way I know for a retail jeweler to stand out is to offer outstanding service. Truth is, most businesses are not run with offering outstanding service as their main objective. This makes it easy to stand out, because most aren't really trying!

The percentage of customers who turn down a repair based on price is approximately 20%. The secret here is that this 20% of customers will say "no" to the repair **REGARDLESS OF WHAT THAT PRICE IS** (unless the price is *ridiculously low*).

Many mass-merchandisers have come to this realization and have adjusted their price beyond "bargain" prices up to more profitable levels. Many retail jewelers have told me that they cannot understand how the chain jewelry stores in the malls charge such high prices for repairs. It's simple. They, too, are acutely aware of this 20% of customers who invariably say "no", no matter what the charge. And they set their prices to appropriate, profitable levels.

KEEP A DIARY

Many of our students have used this as an efficient way of determining prices that the market (your customers) will bear. This is simple to do. Increase your watch battery prices by 25% and keep track of the number of turndowns you receive in a month versus the number of acceptances.

You'll be surprised at the small ratio of turndowns. Unless you write these numbers in your diary, they become greater in your memory than they actually are. The diary removes the guesswork and does not allow us to prejudice the true outcome of adjusting our prices. The facts and figures will speak for themselves.

Many times we allow one customer out of hundreds to dictate the prices we charge. For example, we've all had a customer who went on and on about a high price for a trivial repair. To our detriment, we oftentimes use this harsh memory as the sole data upon which we base a pricing structure. Truth is that a customer who complains about the price of a $10 watch battery also complains about a $5 watch battery! And if you change 2500 watch batteries per year (the national average) the difference is $12,500.00 per year! Too much money to leave on the table for the sake of a few customers who will complain no matter what we charge!

So keep a diary to see the real facts. This will insulate you from injecting your emotions or a cheapskate's perceptions into your pricing structure.

✓ Keep a Sales Diary

During my time as a service center for a very large jewelry store chain, I observed an experiment that was conducted by the company president. Some of his stores charged $3 for batteries and some charged $15 for the same service. He instructed the stores to swap prices; that is, those stores charging $3 were to change to $15 and vice versa. The result was that *the number of battery changes did not change one bit in any store*. Those stores now charging $15 changed as many batteries as they did when they charged $3 and the same was true for those stores now charging $3.

Hard to believe as it may be, the biggest difficulty I have in training jewelers to run successful watch repair departments is their reluctance to take a raise. Many have proudly expressed to me that they charge the same for batteries now as they did 25 years ago. How many of you would love to pay your utility bills at the same rate as 25 years ago, or medications at the same rate as 25 years ago. Why should you charge the same prices now did 25 years ago?

✓ *Take a Raise!*

Thirty years ago my Father's jewelry store was an authorized service center for Timex to Omega. My father's philosophy then was to offer the repairs at cut-rate prices to attract heavy foot traffic, in the hopes that this traffic would convert to sales.

Thirty years ago, this worked. But today there are many other factors that enter in to the equation that nullify this working to your favor. Back then, malls were in their infancy, there was no TV home shopping to compete for your customers, there was no e-commerce (Internet), nor mass-merchandisers (discounters) with their pseudo "75% off" gold sales. If we court their customers with low prices in our repair departments, we are actually subsidizing the part of the industry that cannot offer quality repair in the first place, and asking their customers to use us only for inexpensive repairs while they spend their sales money elsewhere.

✓ *Never Use Repairs as a Loss-Leader*

WATCH BATTERIES

If you are charging $3 - $8 for watch batteries and you are doing every one that comes through your door with no turndowns, you haven't pushed the price envelope far enough to even eliminate any who say "no" no matter what the price. To get to that point, your prices need to be in the $20 - $30 range and will be for a "tune-up" rather than a simple "battery swap". (Tune-up information follows later in this book.)

Even if your results are not typical, that is to say, that perhaps 30% or more say no, the level of service that you will be offering will be without compromise and not easily compared to mass-merchandisers or the corner drug store.

Have no fear in adjusting your prices upward if they are currently too low. Of all the jewelers we have trained to do this, their typical results were that an average of 20% opt to not have the extra service of a "tune-up" done and chose to go down the block to the corner drug store to have the battery swapped by a non-professional. (By the way, many of these customers will come back to you to have the watch repaired after the non-professional has changed the battery and in the process damaged the watch in various ways!) The added profits and prestige available to you for offering "tune-ups" and not "battery swaps" far outweighs the loss of revenue from the low-end customers.

If you only offer a single option for your watch battery customers you are missing out on more than you know.

THE POWER OF 3

Virtually all retail service organizations use some form of selling using the "power of 3". Most of you have been to a car repair place to buy tires or a battery. If you think about that experience you should remember them selling using this method.

One very large retailer uses this method on all their automotive product sales. Here's a hint, " would you prefer a 24 month, 36 month or a 60 month car battery?" This is known as an alternate choice close because it includes the *closing question* with a twist. No matter what they choose, e.g., a 24 month, 36 month or a 60 month battery, the seller wins because the customer bought something -- and they almost *always* choose something!

Here is what most retailers experience using the power of three close, (***even retail jerwelers***).

40% choose the lowest cost option

40% choose the middle price option

20% choose the highest price option

These numbers hold true through most retail business e.g.

Car Repair Shops

Appliance Sales

Car Sales

Furniture Sales (mattress)

Florist

The reason this method of selling works so well is because people are not all the same.

Some people automatically choose the lowest price option no matter what they are offered. This is true of people in all levels of economic strata, rich to poor. The same is true for all 3 choices. If we only offer a single option on the staple repairs we do, like watch batteries, we are missing the boat!

In the next chapter we will cover how to take adventage of the power of 3 with watch batteries.

? Stop Slapping In Batteries and Start Doing Tune-Ups!

REPAIR PRICING

Have your own price list ready for your front counter, based on your watchmaker's prices and what the factory service centers charge, and use that when you prepare the preliminary estimate (Chapter 1). Regardless what those prices are please remember this….. "if it's good for factory service centers, it's good for you". By this I mean if the factory service centers charge $150 to service a watch there is NO GOOD REASON to charge any less. Truth is the factory service centers know their business, they know how to make money, and they should, shouldn't you? The best guide for you and your pricing of watch repairs is the factory service centers. If you see a certain make of watch quite often make it your business to know what their factory service center charges for repairs. All too often jewelers use their competing retail jewelers and what they charge as their sole data for determining repair pricing. WRONG! Most retail jewelers do not operate their repair department for profit! Copying them makes no sense at all. Remember what your mother use to say... "If Bobby jumps off a bridge, I suppose you would too!" If your competitor is loosing money, it makes no sense to copy them! Copy the ones who are *making* money.

If you are basing your pricing on what the outside trade shop charges, you should generally charge triple keystone for watch repairs. There is a formula that you can use. Most of your repairs will be at triple keystone using it, and the most expensive repairs will be done at prices competitive with factory service centers.

- Repairs costing you $100 or less – Triple Keystone
- Repairs costing you $101 to $150 – Keystone + ½
- Repairs costing you over $150 – Straight Keystone

Since most repairs cost you under $100, the bulk of your profits will be at triple keystone. At the same time, your prices on high-end repairs will not be out of line with factory service centers. For repairs you do yourself, such as quartz movement replacements, we suggest 10% of the cost of the watch or 10 times the cost of the movement.

-- 10% of the cost of the watch, e.g., $2500 watch =$250 repair price or a $7 movement cost = $70 repair price.

We must remember that we should never use watch (or any other type of) repair as a loss leader to build traffic. It simply doesn't work. You will only be attracting those customers who are not willing to spend much money. And if they are not willing to spend much money on a repair, what makes you think that they will be willing to spend money on jewelry or anything else we sell.

In today's environment, each and every department within a retail jewelry store must be profitable. Make all the repairs you do profitable and stop doing the ones that aren't. Can you imagine a car dealership discounting car repairs in the vain hopes that they would sell more cars? Of course they would not -- why should they? Do you really think that they would sell more repairs? And if they did, would it affect the sales of cars? The answer is, it would not!

SELLING REPAIRS

CARDINAL SALES RULE #1:

Never Sell Based upon Price.

Price may arise as an objection, and we will deal with responses to that objection later on in this chapter. If a competing retail jeweler is offering repairs at what would essentially be a break-even price, this is no cause for concern.

Price is important, but probably not in the way you think! We must remember the prices we charge are as much a part of our image as the décor we use in our store. My wife Sheila calls this the bait we use. If we only use bottom feeder bait, that's all we will attract.

There are only 5 motivating factors in your customers' minds that cause them to buy anything. These factors can be used singularly or in conjunction with others of those factors.

They are:

PRIDE, PROFIT, NEED, LOVE & FEAR

Retail jewelers traditionally and unconsciously concentrate on explaining to customers why they need to have a repair done. This is ludicrous. No one needs to have a piece of jewelry or a watch repaired.

Even someone who has a need to know what time it is, doesn't necessarily *need* to have a watch to do that. You may believe that he needs a watch for the prestige of it, however, that is not need, that is *pride*.

My father told me long ago that there is nothing we sell in a jewelry store that people can't do without. Actually, if you try to emphasize their need, it brings to mind that they actually don't need it. But when you emphasize pride, for example, they can agree with you. So use the right motivating factor to sell your service products.

✓ *To successfully sell, we must focus on those motivating factors that are truly effective.*

All too often jewelers make the decision for our customer regarding watch repairs. We do this when we presume what our customers will or will not pay to have a watch repaired.

There are times when we see an older watch, e.g., an old Seiko or Bulova that seems to us to have seen better days, and then we talk the customer out of the repair. When we do this we not only risk offending the customer but we are also cheating ourselves out of the possibility of a profitable repair sale. Treat everyone as a viable prospect until they prove to you they are not. The way the prove their viability is when they agree to pay the price we quote.

How can we know the sentimental value or attachment the watch has for the customer and how important getting it repaired is? We can and must know, and the way we find out is through *questioning* the customer.

A good sales presentation is not a situation in which the sales person talks the prospect to death, making statements. Good sales happen when the salesperson asks questions to help the customer obtain what it is that he or she wants!

There are two types of questions we as salesperson can ask. The "open-ended" type question allows the prospect to tell you what they believe to be true. Closed-ended questions

www.watchfix.com
www.watchrepairvideos.com
www.watchrepairbooks.com
www.watchrepairseminars.com

55

enable the prospect give us the answer we need to close the sale. An open-ended question would be, "Do you like this watch?" A close ended question would be, "You like this watch, *don't you?*" or, "You've had this watch a long time, *haven't you?*"

We need to constantly take our customer's temperature during the course of any sale. Taking someone's temperature is also known as "asking qualifying questions".

Take, for example, the customer who came in to your store with an older, automatic, stainless steel Seiko watch. We could just take it from him, go over the preliminary estimate and give him a price, *or we could qualify him.*

Qualifying questions are defined as any question you ask, to which you know what answer *you* want. In the case of watch repairs, the response will show if the customer is sincere about wanting his watch repaired.

Some closed-ended, qualifying questions:

"I'll bet you this watch has a history to it, doesn't it?"

"You must be proud of this fine old watch, aren't you?"

"Someone special gave this to you, didn't they?"

"This is a family heirloom, isn't it?"

"You've had this watch a long time, haven't you?"

"This watch is important to you, isn't it?"

"You are giving this to someone special, aren't you?"

Qualifying questions serve two purposes. First of all, they eliminate the customers who don't really want their watch fixed, by this I mean those who are not sure if they want a watch fixed or to buy a new one. Secondly, the positive answers give you ammunition for closing the sale later and help the customer agree with you.

While you are asking the qualifying question(s), try this: gently nod your head affirmatively (I have never met a customer who could shake their head no while I was nodding my head yes) and make eye contact while you are asking the question. This connects you to the customer and allows him or her to be more comfortable about responding positively.

And, valid or not, it is a common belief that if you make eye contact you are telling the truth.

If they answer negatively (e.g., "Nah, I bought this at Goodwill to wear to work at the construction site."), direct them to your watch sales showcase and sell them a new watch. At this point, they have disqualified themselves from being viable watch repair customers and typically 20% - 30% of those customers actually buy a watch from you, so that you will *still* be making a profit.

There are many retail jewelers who have thousands of dollars tied up in repairs that were never picked up. This, by and large, is because they did not first qualify the customer to determine if he or she was sincere about wanting the watch to be in working order and is willing to pay for the service. Make this the first thing you do when you are handed a watch for repair.

If the customer answers positively to any of those questions (e.g., "It was a present from my husband 20 years ago", or "Yes, I love this watch") they have qualified themselves.

Ask questions. Most of the time people are honest when asked a question, so use it to your advantage. This will also give you fuel to close the sale further on in this process. Even if using qualifying questions automatically disqualifies 20% of your watch repair customers, it does increase your opportunity to sell new watches, as well as increasing your profitability by eliminating sending to and paying for your watchmaker to perform a repair that will never be picked up.

So use qualifying questions. Use this method for jewelry repairs and other sales as well.

✓ *Use Qualifying Questions*

CLOSES

In chapter 1, we touched on the Alternate Choice close and the Order Blank close. Here are some more close types:

Puppy Dog close – this close has been used successfully by luxury car salesmen for years. It goes like this: You have recently visited a luxury car dealership and did not buy a car. On a Friday afternoon you receive a call from the salesman telling you that he'll be going out of town for the weekend and that he would appreciate you doing him a favor. That favor is to park his luxury car in your driveway for safekeeping, and you can have use of car for the weekend. Of course, you agree.

Saturday afternoon you are out cutting your lawn and your neighbor's doing the same. He takes a stroll over to your yard and says, "Wow, I love your new car!" You have two choices – you can tell him the truth, or you can say, "Thanks for noticing."

This, in a nutshell, is the Puppy Dog close (take this puppy dog home for me").

I have a watch repair trade customer who buys and reconditions every older, low cost Rolex and Omega he can get his hands on. When a quality customer comes in to have a watch repaired, he offers them a "loaner". Of course, the loaner is one of these older Rolexes or Omegas.

www.watchfix.com
www.watchrepairvideos.com
www.watchrepairbooks.com
www.watchrepairseminars.com

60

Many times these customers call a few hours after they have dropped off their watch to be repaired to tell him to not repair the watch, but "how much is this watch I'm wearing?"

Add-On close – This close is very effective and predictable. In order to fully take advantage of this type of close, it must be used consistently. Every time a customer agrees to spend money with you, immediately offer them another product or service. Pizza chains use this close very successfully. They train their order takers to ask each customer who has placed an order for pizza, "Do you want any soda with that?" and their soda sales soar.

Jewelers can use this, for example, when a customer has just dropped off a watch to be repaired. Once the transaction has been completed, immediately say something to the effect of, "Can I show you our new line of watches?" Your sales ratio using this close will be in the area of 1 in 7.

Think of all the times someone agrees to give you money, then think of it in terms of every 7th one giving you additional money. However most of my students who use this technique report to me that 1 in 3 buy watchbands, etc.

THANK YOU CARDS

This is a topic in today's society that is completely overlooked. Seldom does anyone in business even verbalize the words "thank you". But savvy business people are using this technique to really stand out. Be sure to thank your customers consistently in your face-to-face meetings with them. The ultimate form of this is to mail a thank you note to them at their home or business.

✓ *BE DIFFERENT – SAY THANK YOU AND SMILE!*

DEALING WITH THE PRICE OBJECTION

Now, let's suppose you have gone through your preliminary estimate and the total comes to $175 at retail. Your customer let's out a gasp at this point and says, *"WHY SO MUCH???"*

You could just say, "Because we do high quality repairs" or "That's what our watchmaker charges." From a psychological standpoint, any statement you make will be challenged in the mind of the customer. Conversely, any question you ask that the customer can agree to is not challenged.

We begin to learn how to challenge statements at a very early age. You know, "My Dad can whoop your Dad", "No he can't." As you know, this cycle can go on for quite some time.

The same is true in a sales interview. If we say, as a categorical statement, "We offer the finest watch repair available anywhere," the customer will automatically think that this is not a true statement.
But if we say to the customer, "We strive to offer the finest watch repairs available, and that's what you want, isn't it?" he can agree with you without feeling challenged.

✓ *Don't make categorical statements by which the customer can feel challenged. Ask questions to which you can both agree.*

DIRECTING THE CONVERSATION

Often our customer's thinking is not based in reality. This can be very hard to overcome with conventional methods. By using the right phrases we can get our customer to concentrate on valid issues.

"I understand how you feel. Many people feel that way until they realize what exactly goes in to a fine watch repair."

"Mr. Customer, is it the price or the cost that you are concerned with? When you buy a low priced item, it doesn't last as long or give the same service as a higher priced like item, making the lower priced item less cost effective."

✓ *Change the Basis of Your Customer's Thinking!*

CLOSE THE SALE

Our customers are desperately looking for someone in whom they can have confidence. We accomplish this when we truly sell to them. If we do not have the confidence to ask the customer for the sale, then we do not inspire confidence. We inspire confidence when we close the sale!

The close is defined as any question we ask to which the affirmative answer means that the customer has bought our product or service. The sales trainer that I had as a young man told me that asking the customer "Are you going to buy that, stupid?" was better than no close at all. Of course, we don't recommend you actually say that! But it brings to light a good example.

Okay, let's try this again: "WHY SO MUCH???" Your response: "You do want it done right, *don't you*?"

You will notice the last two words are underlined and in italics. This is the phrase that makes it easy for the customer to agree with you.

These types of phrases are known as "Socratic Closes", named after the Greek philosopher who spent virtually his entire life *questioning* society.

So, never answer a question with a categorical statement. When our customers ask these types of questions, they are not really posing an objection. They are asking you to show them a benefit that will allow them to say yes.

Many times, even seasoned sales people confuse an objection with a condition. When a customer says, "I can't afford that", this is a condition, (if it's true). You cannot sell over a condition (defined as that which precludes making the sale), such as "I can't afford that" or "I am moving to Mars on Sunday." These are insurmountable conditions.

An objection is any question your customer asks which in effect says "Give me more benefits." Here is a list of some benefits for watch repair customers:

> Your watch will look and run as good as new. (And that's what you want, *isn't it?*)

> You will enjoy knowing that your watch is guaranteed as well as any new watch we sell. (And that's important to you, *isn't it?*)

> You will be proud to give this to your loved one, *won't you?*

Price isn't as important to you as having it done correctly, *is it*?

At this point, your customers will either have agreed with you or not. If they have – and this is important – SHUT UP AND SETTLE THE DETAILS! They have bought the repair in their mind. Your only job at this point is to settle the details (what day to pick it up, etc.).

When you say, "Price isn't as important to you as having it done correctly, *is it*?" and they say, "That's right," *the sale is closed*. Anything you say after that that isn't connected with settling details could cause you to have to re-sell them all over again!

Try using the closed-ended, Socratic closing questions in your everyday life. There are many good reasons for this. By constantly selling (i.e., questioning), these will become ingrained habits and become smooth, fluent and comfortable to you. Some of your largest sales will come from the most unlikely places when you practice this.

www.watchfix.com
www.watchrepairvideos.com
www.watchrepairbooks.com
www.watchrepairseminars.com

67

GOAL SETTING

Virtually all successful retail jewelers set sales goals for their stores. This is important. To quote Winston Churchill, "If we don't know where we're going, any road we take will get us there." So have a goal. If your store already uses goal setting, be sure to include watch (and jewelry) repairs in those goals. Make the goals realistic, but also make them something to strive for.

Personal goal setting is as important as business goal setting and they must work hand in hand. That is, the realization of the business goals will enable the successful realization of personal goals.

MOTIVATING YOUR STAFF

Unfortunately, many jewelers who offer commission to their sales help do not include repairs in the commission structure. This can be very counterproductive. I have personally seen this situation result in sales help referring away or not giving watch repair customers the attention they deserve. What could have been a profitable repair sale and a new potential merchandise customer is often slighted so that the sales person could get back to the sales floor where he or she could make some commission.

One of our students has put into effect this "spiff" program for his sales people: The Mayonnaise Jar. Each time a salesperson correctly takes a watch in for repair, his or her name is written on a $1 bill, which is placed in a very large mayonnaise jar in the break area for all to see. At the end of the year, $1 is removed and the person whose name is on that bill gets the contents of the jar. This gets the staff *very* excited about properly taking in repairs!

Include repairs in your commission structure as well as a repair sales quota for all your sales staff to strive for and to achieve.

www.watchfix.com
www.watchrepairvideos.com
www.watchrepairbooks.com
www.watchrepairseminars.com

69

Taking Action

✓ Review Chapter 1 and Ensure that You Have Put All Concepts Into Practice

✓ Make the Commitment that Your Store will Offer the Finest Watch Repair Service in Your Market Area

✓ Create a Front Counter Price Guide for Your Store

✓ Treat Every Watch Repair Customer as an Important Customer

✓ Practice Qualifying Questions with Your Staff

✓ Practice Closing Questions with Your Staff

✓ Set Watch Repair Sales Goals for your Store and Individually for Your Sales Staff

Chapter 3
Marketing – Taking Advantage of Your Advantages

WATCH BATTERIES – THE KEY TO GREAT PROFITS

Why am I going to spend a great deal of time now on the "lowly" watch battery – and in the Marketing Section, to boot? Because I know that this 24¢ investment can reap for you not only astronomical profit to cost ratios, but they are the entryway for your clients to learn who you are and why they should come back to your store for exceptional services - which can and will convert into sales.

98% of all watches sold today contain watch batteries. This creates an enormous reservoir of potential customers. The only reason retail customers would frequent radio stores, discount stores, hardware stores and drug stores for watch batteries is if there is no difference between them and you. If all we do is slap in a battery, then we are not worth any more than the aforementioned retailers are.

As we have stated earlier, we must make it our strict policy to offer uncompromisingly excellent service. This automatically sets us apart from the crowd of retailers who

www.watchfix.com
www.watchrepairvideos.com
www.watchrepairbooks.com
www.watchrepairseminars.com

72

offer minimum services at minimum charges. Retail jewelers must and should be the place where professionalism and craftsmanship are of utmost importance.

If all we are doing is prying the back off the watch, shoving a battery in and pressing the back on, we are risking our reputation as professionals for very few dollars in return. Radio stores, drug stores and others can afford to risk their reputations as battery swappers. That is not what they are known for. You in the jewelry trade cannot and should not risk yours for the $5.

It's easy to look at watch batteries in the narrow view. Everyone from battery stores to drugstores to department stores, hardware stores and yes, even most other retail jewelers look at it that way. To them it is just a "pain in the neck" service that they are obliged to perform, whether they know how to perform it or not. Every one of those retailers can relate awful scenarios that go along with doing business this way.

www.watchfix.com
www.watchrepairvideos.com
www.watchrepairbooks.com
www.watchrepairseminars.com

73

I recently heard of a discount department store that pried the back off a Piaget Polo. This particular watch has a crown on the back to set the hands with. It also has gold screws that hold the back on. It seems the sales clerk didn't really look at the watch before prying the back off with a case knife -- breaking the stem and the crown and shearing the tops off gold screws. The store had to replace the watch, at a cost of $16,000.

THIS CREATES AN ENORMOUS OPPORTUNITY FOR YOU!

Because of these types of circumstances, many of the aforementioned retailers have opted to no longer offer or at least severely curtail their services in this area. Exploit this!

USE YOUR COMPTEITORS TO YOUR ADVANTAGE

This next idea will require some bravado at first. Please do not formulate any pre-conceived notions on the course of action that I am going to lay out for you here. It is a natural inclination for many people, when asked to perform outside of their "comfort zone", to do nothing, take no action and profit nothing from it!

But YOU are special and unique, or you need to be! You have chosen to stand out from the crowd. This requires you to stretch that comfort zone you are in and do things that you would not ordinarily do, in order to reap the benefits beyond.

Imagine asking your competitors (e.g., battery stores, drug stores, etc.) to collectively give you $25,000 to $75,000 over the course of a year. Betcha' they wouldn't do it.

But I am telling you -- and you must absolutely believe what I am going to tell you – they will!

Department Stores, Drug Stores, Hardware Stores, Battery Stores

It has come to my attention recently, by way of one of our students, that one of the big "-Mart" chains (insert whatever prefix you feel appropriate) has ceased to offer watch batteries or jewelry repairs of any kind as of August 1, 1999. They are currently looking for businesses in all market areas to which they can refer their customers. I predict that this trend will be followed by virtually all your competitors in this field. It is already happening *de facto* among all the rest.

Take a bold step

This part is very simple. It does, however, require some bravado the first time out. Go through your local yellow pages and make a list of all the businesses in your area that change watch batteries. Visit all of them with a smile on your face and a box of business cards in your hand. The cards should look something like this:

www.watchfix.com
www.watchrepairvideos.com
www.watchrepairbooks.com
www.watchrepairseminars.com

76

```
ABC Jewelers
123 Main St., Anytown, USA
_____

Watch Batteries Expertly Installed

                              Directions on Back
```

```
Directions:

Left out of Parking Lot to Elm St.
Right on Elm St.,
Two Blocks to Stop Sign,
ABC Jewelers on Corner of Elm and Main
```

You want to make up special business cards, just for this purpose. One reason for this is that you want to be able to measure your response from this effort (and you will be amazed!).

Notice that on the front there is no phone number. The customer must come to see you. Also, be sure not to put anything threatening on the front (or back) of the card, such as "Diamonds at Wholesale Prices" or "Your Diamond Expert". This would tend to alienate the retailer you are going to ask to give you business.

The back enables the customer to easily get to your store from the location at which he or she received the card. You may even want to draw a map on the back.

When you enter the department store, do it at a time at which the jewelry department manager will be in. Ask to see only the jewelry department manager (NOT the Store Manager). Have a pleasant smile on your face when you meet this individual.

Tell him or her that you are from your jewelry store (by name) and that you specialize in installing watch batteries professionally, even those that are very difficult to do. Tell him or her that you just dropped by to let them know that you are in the area and that you are willing to take care of any battery installation difficulties they may have, that you also take links out of bands, replace crystals and do general watch repairs.

At this point – and this is important – hand them the cards and *shut up*.

In most cases the department manager will say, "Great!" -- and your job is done.

In the cases of the hundreds of jewelers I have instructed to do this, not a single one has related back to me any negative experience whatsoever! The reports I have received, and my own experiences with this, have been overwhelmingly positive. Try to see it from their eyes, watch batteries are a pain in the neck for a $5.25 per hour store clerk at best!

Usually the jewelry department manager is thrilled to know where they can send customers who ask for services that can get the store into difficulties!

Be an answer to someone else's prayer and answer your own at the same time!

Other Retail Jewelers

Don't make the presumption that other retail jewelers in your town don't also get into battery difficulties and situations they would rather not attempt.

I strongly advise you visit every jeweler in your market area and give them the good news about your battery work as well.

With a fellow retail jeweler, you have some commonality and can go into more depth about business in general, and mention that you specialize in problem watch batteries, quartz watch repair, as well as all other watch repairs.

Be non-specific about your services as to not be threatening, but answer any direct question the other jeweler may have. It only takes one retail jeweler who refers his "problems" to you to add thousands of dollars to your bottom line.

✓ *Use Your Competitors to Your Advantage*

Don't Slap In a Battery – Do a *"Tune-Up"*

A Harvard professor was once quoted as saying, "Unless a man has trained himself for his chance, the chance will only make him look ridiculous."

If you have followed the previous steps, you now have a great stream of battery traffic coming into your store. Now, make that traffic truly profitable, while building your reputation as a watch and jewelry professional who offers outstanding service.

Anyone can figure out how to open a watch (not always correctly, as we have seen earlier!) and replace the battery. What will make you stand out is to offer a *Watch Tune-Up*, which includes the following:

> Replace the battery
> Clean the case and band
> Replace of the Crystal (if appropriate)
> Silicone the gasket
> Silicone the stem & tube
> Proper Closure of the Case
> Warranty the work for a full year

The technique for performing the tune-up is demonstrated on the videotape, " A Course in Profits Through Service: TUNE-UPS" (If you do not have a copy, please let us know.) Be sure to mark the inside of the case back with an ultra-fine point "sharpie" with the date of the tune-up.

Here arc the tools and supplies you will need to perform tune-ups:

BACK GASKETS – Most good watch material houses have low cost gaskets assortments. A good assortment will have several different sizes.

O-RING GASKET SPEED LUBRICATOR - This is the "added touch" that makes what you will be doing worth more than what "they" are doing. Simple to use, you place the gasket in the container, twist the cover, and the job is done for you.

CASE SILICONE -- You will also need a tube of silicone to seal water-resistant models. Place some silicone (A white, greasy substance) around the case tube (the part of the case that the crown fits over).

www.watchfix.com
www.watchrepairvideos.com
www.watchrepairbooks.com
www.watchrepairseminars.com

82

A QUALITY CASE PRESS – This may seem like a no-brainer, but you would be surprised how many jewelers do not have one or have one so inferior that many crystals are broken and cases damaged in closing the watch. A case press priced in the $40 to $50 should suffice; it should have both metal and plastic cups.

A QUALITY UNIVERSAL CASE WRENCH – You will need the type of adjustable wrench that enables you to open screw-on backs.

A QUALITY SET OF SCREWDRIVERS – You want to have the type of screwdriver set that has removable and replaceable blades.

A PAIR OF PLASTIC TWEEZERS – self explanatory.

A PAIR OF NON-MAGNETIC, STAINLESS STEEL TWEEZERS – 3C, 3, 3A -- as long as they are non-magnetic.

ASSORTMENT OF ROUND, MINERAL GLASS (MG) CRYSTALS – these are the round, flat crystals, used in many watches today, they cost around $1.00 and you can sell them for $35.00.

ULTRAVIOLET GLUE – this glue dries clear as glass. It can dry in direct sunlight or under an ultraviolet lamp. Your watch material supply house offers a crystal assortment, UV glue and UV lamp package at a very reasonable price.

GS HYPO CRYSTAL GLUE – this is rubber cement, for plastic crystals. It has a hypodermic-type applicator.

An ILLUSTRATED QUARTZ MOVEMENT CATALOG – self explanatory.

GS CRYSTAL CATALOG – self explanatory.

GEM SINGLE EDGE RAZOR BLADES – (Be careful!)

CASE KNIFE – Self explanatory.

DIAMOND SHARPENING STONE – you should be able to get one of these at any local sporting goods store for around $10. It is used for sharpening your knife, tweezers and screwdrivers. It will last indefinitely.

When you do a "tune-up" (rather than a "battery swap") you place yourself in the top 1% of those offering excellent service. We are the professionals. If we are to be viewed as such by our clients, we should do a professional job in everything we do, including a battery change.

We have found that a fair price for this new service is in the range of $20 – 40, depending on your market.

Even if you eliminate 50% of your watch battery business (don't worry, this won't happen), by charging this price for the added service you will still be making many times more than if you changed every battery that came in the door at your usual $5-$7.

The following is a sign that one of our students put in his store. He was previously charging $5 for watch batteries and considered it an annoyance. He now averages $29 on his watch battery business, offering his customers a variety of services.

Tune Up Service $39.^{95}

- *Lifetime battery*
- *Replace gaskets*
- *Silicone seal stem & crown*
- *Clean band & case*
- *Polish crystal (if possible)*
- *1 yr. warranty on work*

Lifetime Battery $25.^{00}

1 Year Battery $10.^{00}

Customer satisfaction will soar, as will your reputation as a professional.

Think of all the times that you changed a battery for someone who came back a month or two later to tell you that his watch used to be water resistant, but now is getting condensation when he cuts the grass or works outside. This could have been avoided by adding the "tune-up" service to your menu.

You may opt to offer multi-level services, that is, a $10 one-year battery without the extra tune-up services, a $25 "lifetime" battery (if they come back for the free battery for more than 5 years, it will be the rare case), or the Tune-up service at $39.

Some of you may opt to have several pricing options for your customers. Going back to what we discussed in Chapters 1 & 2, we must offer the finest service of which we are capable and be paid for it.

THE BEST 23 CENTS YOU'LL SPEND

Regardless of what type of battery installations or tune-ups you do, here is a great traffic builder for your store:

Go to the post office and purchase a large quantity of post cards. Have a rubber stamp made or have the postcards professionally printed, or print them yourself on your computer or by hand with this message:

Don't run out of TIME!

It's been nearly a year since we replaced the battery in your watch. Please stop by so that we can take care of this for you.

Sincerely,
Store Owner

Get the battery or tune-up customer's name and address, and put it on the address side of the postcard.

Place that postcard in a monthly "tickler file" for 11 months in the future. Then mail that postcard in that 11th month. The repeat business garnered by this is enormous!

This tactic can be applied to jewelry repairs as well. Set up a postcard file for 6 months after doing any work on diamond jewelry. Offer to check the diamond's safety and clean the piece for free.

This bit of marketing comes from the quick-car-lube industry. Three months after your oil and lube, they send you a post card, reminding you to come back again. Isn't it a good idea for you, too?

LOW COST ADVERTISING THAT WORKS

What if I told you that you could run a classified ad in your Sunday paper that could net you thousands of dollars over the course of the year? You would do it, wouldn't you? Of course you would! Here is one:

```
ANTIQUE JEWELRY

Buying, Selling, Trading, Repairing
Rolex Watches. ABC Jewelers, 123 Main St.,
Anytown, USA. Not affiliated with Rolex
USA.
```

This little ad is dynamite! It costs very little. You only run it once per week, in the Sunday Classifieds.

Different newspapers have different classifications. You may want to place it in Antique Jewelry, Watches, Jewelry or the appropriate classification in your area.

This ad employs a very powerful marketing principal. It is, if you advertise the highest of your abilities, it is assumed that you posses all abilities leading to that. In other words, if you are good enough to deal in Rolex Watches, it is implied that you must be able to deal with all other watches as well. (In the eyes of most of the public, Rolex Watches are among the highest grade of watches.)

The second principal that is employed in this ad is that it covers a lot of ground with very few words: "Buying, Selling, Trading, Repairing". It says you do it all.

There are many people who would love to own a Rolex watch, or another high-grade watch, who search the classifieds looking for a "great deal". Being in the classified ads puts you in front of these people as well as probate attorneys, estate liquidators, folks who have recently undergone economic turmoil, etc.

www.watchfix.com
www.watchrepairvideos.com
www.watchrepairbooks.com
www.watchrepairseminars.com

90

How would you like to have a probate attorney call you with 6 Rolex watches that he needs to liquidate, or some such situation? This does happen, as well as bringing in those who are looking to buy, sell, or have a Rolex Watch or other high-grade watch repaired.

WINDOW SIGNAGE

Over the past several years, many jewelers have successfully trained their customers to expect a complete lack of service. This gives us the opportunity to inform customers that services *are still* available -- and at your store. We must remember that a jewelry store is a visual environment, people come there to see things, so show them! Use signs to your advantage, all well run stores do -- jewelry stores and other successful stores as well.

That can be accomplished with something as basic as a modest sign (flat or neon) in your window that simply says, "Watch Repairs". Twenty years ago, this would not have been necessary, but today it absolutly is.

LOOKING THE PART

Is there a part of your store that tells your customers that you perform watch repairs?

If you have limited space, a sign, perhaps hanging from the ceiling over an area where you will usually take in watch repairs, is very advantageous. Believe it or not, you probably have customers coming into your store on a daily basis who have no idea that you offer watch repair services. Tell them with a sign.

Years ago I worked at a bench that was enclosed in glass, between all the watch counters in the store. Most jewelers did it that way then. But because so few jewelers today have a watchmaker working on their premises, that space has been made available for other things.

I realize that many of you do not have the space available to put a bench and all the accouterments on valuable floorspace.

If you are lucky enough to have space for a watch bench on your sales floor, never allow clutter or disorganization to appear on it.

Keep it looking as professional as your diamond room or counter. On it should be only tweezers, screwdrivers, a case press, and a loupe or visor. It has greater value for appearance sake than for utility.

✓ *ATTITUDE IS EVERYTHING*

I can tell you that when I worked in a retail environment, everyone who entered the store automatically presumed I was the watchmaker because of one tell-tale sign: I wore a loupe on my glasses.

Years ago, we called the person who did not actually do repairs but took in the repairs in such a way that everyone presumed him to be the watchmaker, a "frontman". (Today that position would be called a "Frontperson".) The only thing that made them a frontperson was appearance.

It is our responsibility to inspire the customers' confidence in our professionalism.

Have those of your staff who handle watch repairs interface with the watch repair customer *at the watch repair bench or area*, wearing a loupe, and taking their time to study the watch as if it were something very important. It is to your customer. It should be to you.

TAKING ACTION

✓ Make a list of all local retailers who presently do watch batteries.

✓ Have business cards made especially for watch battery referrals.

✓ Make time to visit with all retailers on your list.

✓ Have all the tools and supplies necessary to do first-class watch battery business (Tune-Ups).

✓ Keep a diary of your prices as you edge them up, and keep track of the ratio of those who refuse the service, against those who say yes.

✓ Prepare for sending battery reminder postcards.

✓ Place the classified ad.

✓ Make or have made window signage.

Chapter 4
What Makes It Tick?

You can be the most proficient marketer or salesperson on earth, but if you don't know the ins and outs of the product you are selling or for which you are selling the service, you can't instill confidence in your clients and you won't keep them very long. In order to really sell a product or service, product knowledge is the key.

Please give this chapter its due attention. Without this knowledge, we become just talking heads selling something that we know little about. Many of you are already aware that in diamond sales, having taken some GIA courses helps immensely. The same is true with watches.

I am often taken aback in my dealings with retail jewelers to find that many do not know even the simplest of terms. In order to be worth more we must not only do more, but also KNOW more than our competition.

This chapter will enable you to enhance your reputation as the "watch professional" in your area. In addition to some general watch terms that relate to the exterior of a watch, we will explain each major part of a mechanical watch and what function it performs.

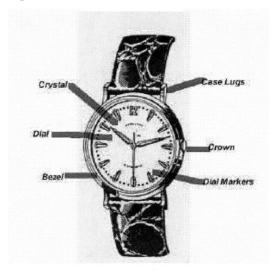

First, let's go over the outside of the watch.

Crown – the "knob" used to wind the watch.

Crystal – the glass or plastic covering over the dial and hands.

Bezel – the part of the case that holds the crystal on.

Dial – sometimes called the "face".

Dial Markers – slashes or numbers noting the time.

Case Lugs – part of the case onto which the band is attached with spring bars.

Illustrated Listing of the Major Parts of a Watch Movement

As a basic guideline, "pinions push, wheels follow." You'll understand as you read on.

Crown

The Crown is the winding knob on the outside of the watch, usually at the 3:00 position on a wristwatch. There are three basic types of crowns. They are:

Dustproof - This type of crown has a spring-loaded bushing that rests against the case to prevent dust from entering the case. This type of crown has NO WATER RESISTANCE characteristics what so ever! They are generally used on older types of watches or newer dress watches, and are also know as dress crowns.

www.watchfix.com
www.watchrepairvideos.com
www.watchrepairbooks.com
www.watchrepairseminars.com

100

Waterproof or O-ring - These are the types of crowns in which the crown has a recess that fits over a tube on the case. The O-ring or gasket fits snugly over the tube forming a tight, water-resistant seal.

Screw Down - This is the type of crown used in the situation in which the crown and case tube are both threaded. This crown screws on to the case tube. When properly screwed down, this type of crown has the greatest capabilities for water resistance.

Stem

WINDING STEM   Also know as a winding arbor.   This is sometimes called a winder, but that is only part of what it does. The stem is the part of the watch that attaches to the Crown.   The stem has the following functions: 1) it connects to the crown and; 2) enables the watch to be wound and set.

Detent/Set Lever

SET LEVER   The detent, also known as set lever, has two functions. First, it secures the stem in the watch. Secondly, the detent shifts the watch from the wind position to the set position by shifting the set lever.

Clutch Lever

CLUTCH LEVER   This part rests in the channel in the clutch and engages the stetting mode when the detent shifts it. The set lever pushes the clutch into the setting wheel, allowing the hands to be set by turning the stem.

Clutch

CLUTCH WHL   Also know as a sliding pinion. This is the part that disengages or slides on the stem out of the winding mode when the detent pushes the set lever into the set position and engages the setting wheel.

Winding Pinion

WINDING PINION The winding pinion mates with the crown wheel and the crown wheel mates with the ratchet wheel to wind the main spring.

Setting Wheel

Bevel Pinion Also know as an intermediate setting wheel or beveled pinion. This part connects with the clutch at one end and the minute wheel at the other end. When it is engaged it enables the hands to be set.

Minute Wheel

260 MINUTE WHL This part connects the setting wheel at one end and the cannon pinion at the other. It makes one full revolution every 60 minutes.

Cannon Pinion

Ratchet Wheel

RATCHET WHL   This part connects to the crown wheel at one end and the mainspring arbor at the other.

Crown Wheel

CROWN WHEEL   This part connects with the winding pinion at one end and the and on the other side connects to the ratchet wheel, as part of the winding mechanism.

Third Wheel

3RD WHEEL   Third wheel is a gear ratio wheel that connects to the center wheel and the fourth wheel.

Fourth Wheel

4TH WHL NO SEC BI7 The fourth wheel is also a ratio wheel, connecting to the third wheel at one end and the escape wheel at the other.

Escape Wheel

PIN ESCAPE WHL PIVOTED S/S The escape wheel connects to the fourth wheel at one end and to the pallet fork at the other.

Balance Wheel

BALANCE COMP FLAT

ROLLER **BALANCE STAFF INCA**

www.watchfix.com www.watchrepairbooks.com
www.watchrepairvideos.com www.watchrepairseminars.com

The Balance wheel, or more correctly, balance complete, has several parts. They are: the hairspring, the balance staff, and the roller table with roller jewel.

Pallet Fork

This part has the escape wheel at one end and the roller table and roller jewel at the other end. It is the central part of the "Lock and Slide" process, explained on the following page...

Put them all together...

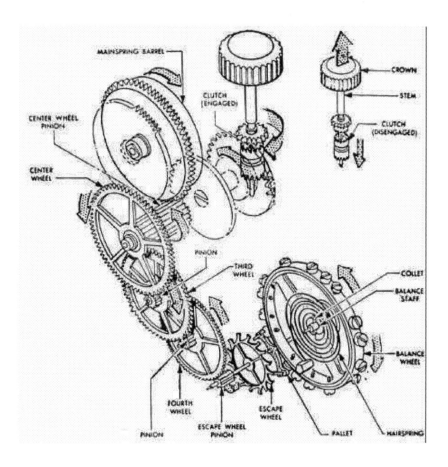

The pallet fork has two forces acting upon it. First, the force of the tightened mainspring makes the escape wheel push on the pallet fork, which, because of the design of the escape wheel teeth, locks the escape wheel into place each time a tooth passes it.

As the pallet fork is moving into that locked position, it hits the roller jewel, which is attached to the roller table, which is attached to the balance wheel, making the balance wheel spin on the balance staff (pivot).

The hairspring within the balance wheel tightens, causing a re-action of uncoiling. The balance wheel swings back in the opposite direction, knocking (by way of the roller table and roller jewel) the pallet fork out of the **lock** position and allowing the escape wheel to **slide** the space of one more tooth. This knocking back and forth creates the ticking sound of the watch.

The length of the hairspring regulates the length of time that this process takes, which is how we determine how fast or slow the watch runs.

www.watchfix.com
www.watchrepairvideos.com
www.watchrepairbooks.com
www.watchrepairseminars.com

111

Now you understand the basic parts and the fundamental principals under which a mechanical watch operates. Begin using these terms in your daily interactions with your customers and they will become second nature to you.

Here are some other types of mechanical movements:

- Automatic, also known as self-winding or a "perpetual" watch – This type of watch has a semi-circular weight that winds the watch by using the inertia of the wearer's bodily motion to wind the watch. Unlike quartz watches, this type of watch must be constantly worn to remain running.

- Calendar watch -- This watch has a window on the dial that displays the date and/or day and/or month, or an arrow that points to these.
- Alarm watch – An alarm watch that, in addition to keeping time, can act as an alarm clock on the wrist.
- Chronograph – This is a watch that has more than one timekeeping feature, for example, one that tells time and has a stopwatch built in to it.

If the information contained in this part of the book is old hat to you, use it as a refresher. If not, study this section well. It will help you in many ways. Not only will it help you to sell to the customer, but it will also help you to interface with your watchmaker, and, believe me, being able to speak the same language helps more than you know!

Chapter 5

Simple Quartz Watch Repairs

You Can Do In Your Store

Quartz watch service is an area in which the retail jeweler can really stand out from the competition. Offer unparalleled service and make a very good profit in the process.

Please, have no reservations about this. As you recall in previous chapters, we discussed expanding outside of your comfort zone. And I presume you have. By now you have found the benefits associated with doing so. This part of the book will cover 95% of the quartz watch problems you will encounter. Your watch repair trade shop can handle the remaining 5%. It is possible in many cases to enjoy a 1000% mark-up on these services. Try to refrain from feeling guilty about this. The old adage goes, "find the need and fill it, is the foundation of good business." And there definitely is the need. If we compare the pricing charged by Factory Repair Centers, we will find that they charge $65 for the service on a major brand fashion watch with an ESA 578.004 movement. The movement that replaces this, the Harley 751 E, costs $9.95. This is a direct replacement (that is, the hands and dials all match up – more on this later) of equivalent quality. That is a 600% markup. If we luxuriate and take our time, this job shouldn't take more than 20 minutes. With the profit being $50, that's $150 per hour. Not bad, eh?

TOOLS & SUPPLIES

These can be purchased from your watch material supply house. (see appendix)

- Pair of Tweezers
- Screwdrivers
- Hand Removers
- Dial Dots & Strips
- Speedi Fit / Retro Eze
- File
- Scalpel
- Side Cutter Pliers
- Hand Blower / Canned Air
- Pin Vice
- Crystal Glue – GS Glue, Rocket Glue or UV Glue
- Paintbrush
- Vigor Circuit Maker
- Can of Plasticlean
- Quartz Movement Catalog
- Assortment of Crowns

- Hand Assortment

- Quarts Watch Pulse Tester. For those of you who are taking this seriously I recommend the Witschi Cyclonic Rate, this machine has a digital display that shows the timing of the watch. Remember that the customers believe what they see, and this machine SHOWS THEM!

- Movement Ligne Gauge / Scale

A movement number identifies all quartz movements. Let's presume that for the purposes of this exercise, you have used a loupe and identified the model number of the movement you are replacing. This number can always be found somewhere on the movement side (the side where the battery goes, the part you see when you remove the back of the watch) of the movement (the obverse of the dial side). This number can be found stamped into the metal of the movement, or engraved or stamped onto the circuitry, e.g., "ESA 955.112". You will notice in the quartz movement catalog that manufacturer segregates the movements. They are:

- ETA / ESA - some of the companies that use these movements are:

- Omega
- Longines
- Concord
- Movado
- Bulova
- Piaget
- Certina
- Ebel
- Hamilton

- FE – this stands for "Francais Ebauche", which means, "Made in France". They are used by:
  - Benrus
  - Gucci
  - Many "off-brands"

- Harley/Ronda – Are also used by many "Off-Brands"

- Hatori – This is a Japanese made movement, used most often in:
  - Seiko
  - Pulsar

- Sharp
- Lasalle
- Lorus

- ISA Used in many low-cost quartz watches. Among them:
  - Swiss Army
  - Wenger
  - Marlboro

- Miyota – A Japanese made movement used in:
  - Citizen
  - Bulova
  - Caravelle

- Remex – a Chinese movement used on many inexpensive watches

How to Use the Quartz Movement Catalog:
You should have a Quartz Movement Catalog. Most good material houses can supply one to you at N/C.

The following is an abstract explanation of the terms you will find in most movement catalogs.

- **Caliber** denotes the number found on the movement.
- **Price** is what the movement will cost you.
- **Ligne Size** is a watchmaker's measurement of the width and length of the movement.
- **Millimeter Diameter** is measured at the widest point of the movement.
- **Thickness** (in millimeters) (self-explanatory).
- **Dial Feet** indicates the position of the posts on the back of the dial. These posts attach the dial to the movement.
- **Hands** indicate the millimeter size of the hole in the hands, so that they fit correctly over the post.
- **Cell** denotes the Energizer Cell equivalent.
- **Stem** denotes the Bestfit stem part number (Bestfit is a part cataloging system for all watches).
- **Tap** indicates the thread width of the stem. This will correspond to the thread width in the crown, so that the crown can be screwed correctly onto the stem.

www.watchfix.com
www.watchrepairvideos.com
www.watchrepairbooks.com
www.watchrepairseminars.com

120

Replacing an Exact Exchange Movement

NOTE: ALL ILLUSTRATIONS FOLLOW THE TEXT
AT THE END OF THIS CHAPTER.

In most cases, you will be replacing a movement for which you will have found an exact match movement, e.g., an ESA 955.112 for an ESA 955.112.

In that case, the procedure is:

1. Remove the old movement from the case. In some cases, this will necessitate removing the stem.

    - If we look closely at the part of the movement that the stem goes in to, we will notice one of the following conditions: there will be an arrow pointing to a post or button (Fig. 1). In the case of the post or button (Fig. 2), gently press down on it and pull on the stem. Or,

    - There will be an indentation and a lever on the outside perimeter of the movement (Fig. 3). Pull out the lever just far enough to release the stem. Or,

- There will be a small diameter screw-head, just slightly off to the side from the stem.   In the case of the screw, turn the screw only one full turn, and then gently pull on the stem. If it does not release at this point, give it ½ more turn, until it does release.

We will now presume the movement has been removed from the case. Next we need to remove the hands.

2. The most recommended way that hand removal can be accomplished is with bow hand removers.

- Place a clear piece of plastic over the dial and hands (such as a single sheet from an open and separated zip lock bag) or a Mylar or nylon strip can be placed between the dial and hands. This is to protect the dial from being scratched.

- Place the opening of the hand remover over the post holding the hands (cannon pinion), resting on the protected dial.

www.watchfix.com
www.watchrepairvideos.com
www.watchrepairbooks.com
www.watchrepairseminars.com

122

- As you squeeze the bow, the metal jaws will slide under the hands, lifting them off the post.
- Carefully put the hands to one-side, in a safe place, such as a small tray.

3. Removing the Dial – There are several ways in which the dial may be attached to the movement.

   - Dial Hooks (Fig. 4). These are found on the outer perimeter of the movement that attaches the dial to the movement, by pressuring the dial feet in place. To remove this type of dial, use a screwdriver to grab onto the nub at the outer end of the hook and swing the hook out only far enough to loosen the dial foot. If you pull too far, it will remove the hook itself.
   - Eccentric Dial Screws (Fig. 5, Fig. 6) are another method for attaching the dial to the movement. This screw has a cam-shaped head. You will notice that when you turn this screw, only a portion of the screw head pressures against the dial post on the movement side. To remove the dial, turn the screw such that the cam portion no longer rests against the dial post. You will then be able to lift the dial off the movement.

www.watchfix.com
www.watchrepairvideos.com
www.watchrepairbooks.com
www.watchrepairseminars.com

123

- Traditional Dial Screws are located on the *side* of the movement and should be turned only enough to loosen the dial posts.

- Some dials are frictioned in with a piece of Mylar tubing over the dial feet and in the dial positioner holes. If this is the case, the dial will lift off with just a prying with a screwdriver blade between the movement and the dial. If it does not easily lift off, look for another method of attachment, e.g. hooks, screws, etc.

4. The hour wheel is located under the dial, in the center of the watch, on the canon pinion. In some movements, the hour wheel is under the plate and is not removable. If the hour wheel is included with and already installed on the replacement movement, continue on to the next step. If it is not, remove the hour wheel from the old movement and place it safely to one side.

Place the old movement somewhere that it can be available to be used as a template for Speedi Fit (more on this later).

www.watchfix.com
www.watchrepairvideos.com
www.watchrepairbooks.com
www.watchrepairseminars.com

124

Now the hands, dial, hour wheel (if necessary) and stem have been removed. It is time to replace these parts on the new movement, and re-install the movement into the case.

5. Remove the stem that comes with the new movement and place it away for future use. (A little organization of parts goes a long way.)

6. If necessary, place the hour wheel in the movement over the canon pinion.

7. Line up the dial over the dial positioner holes on the movement and tighten it's fasteners.

8. Place the hands back onto the watch.

    First place the hour hand pointing to 9 (if you are right handed. If you are left handed, point the hour hand at 3) over the hour wheel, which is sticking up through the dial, resting on the canon pinion.

9. Taking care to not press the hour wheel too far down (there should be a space between the hand and the dial), use the tweezers to press the hour hand down around the hub of the hour wheel. Place the minute hand on the canon pinion and point it to 12, so that the hands read either 9:00 or 3:00. Make sure you have the hands at a

www.watchfix.com
www.watchrepairvideos.com
www.watchrepairbooks.com
www.watchrepairseminars.com

125

90-degree angle and that they are exactly pointing to the 9 and the 12.

10. With a hand blower or canned air, blow out the dial and crystal so that there is no dust or particles there.

11. Place the movement into the case and, unless the stem was rusted or damaged in some way, place the stem into the watch all the way until it clicks into place. (Instructions for fitting a stem follow.)

12. Now turn the hands using the crown to ensure that the hands clear each other. This is a good use for the Witschi Cyclonic. You can make the hands turn 24 hours to be sure of hand clearance. If they do not clear, remove the movement and adjust the hands, taking care not to scratch the dial.

You have now completed a quartz movement replacement!

www.watchfix.com
www.watchrepairvideos.com
www.watchrepairbooks.com
www.watchrepairseminars.com

126

Replacing an Equivalent Sized Movement

Up to this point we have been dealing with "apples to apples" movement replacement. There are many cases in which the exact type of movement in a watch is not available, or you may be replacing a mechanical movement with a quartz movement.

In this case, we need to determine the size of the original movement. This is done with a ligne gauge. Say, for example, that you have a watch with a Bulova 6BM mechanical movement. Placing the ligne gauge across the width and length of you movement, you will find this is a 6-3/4 x 8 ligne movement.

There are many quartz movements of this dimension to choose from, one of which is the ETA 802.004 movement. Its measurements are 6-3/4 x 8 lignes, however, the dial feet are positioned at 3:30 and 8:30 (as opposed to the Bulova 6BM with the dial feet at 8:00 and 4:00). Also, the Bulova 8BM hands do not match up to the ETA 802.004 movement, and the stem is not the same.

But the movement does fit the case like a glove. To convert this mechanical movement to quartz:

1. Remove the old movement from the case and remove the hands, dial and stem as above.

2. Take the dial and using your sidecutters, clip off the dial feet. Then use your file to carefully remove any nub of the dial feet left on the dial.

3. Place the new movement with the new stem already in it into the caseback, and place the caseback into the bezel. Close the case.

4. Estimate the length the stem will need to stick out from the case to accommodate the crown being screwed on to it.

5. Using your sidecutters, gently mark the stem by pressing on the stem just enough to allow you to see where you need to cut the stem. **Do not cut the stem at this point, while it is still in the case.**

6. Remove the back, remove the movement, and remove the marked stem.

7. Place the stem firmly into your pin vice with the plastic shipping crown sticking out and, using your sidecutters, cut the stem where you have marked it. *Be careful – the*

*part of the stem you are cutting off can be a dangerous
projectile. Never point it at your or others' faces.*

8. Carefully file the cut end of the stem into a cone shape, just enough to smooth the mangled threads at the end of the stem, so that the crown can be easily installed.

9. While the stem is still in the pin vice, get a tap 10 crown of appropriate color and type (dustproof, etc.), and screw it on to the end of the stem.

10. Remove the stem and crown from the pin vice and place it back into the new movement.

11. Place the movement back into the caseback.

12. Place the caseback into the bezel.

13. Check to see if the crown is too long or short for the case.

   - If it is too long, remove the stem, put it back into the pin vice, remove the crown and re-cut the stem.
   - If it is too short, get another stem and start over.
   - NOTE: It does take some practice to estimate the length of the stem. Better long and re-cuttable than too short.

With this process completed, we are ready to attach the dial to the movement.

14. Using your tweezers, remove a single dial dot with the covering paper from the dial dot strip.

15. Place the dial dot onto the dial side of the movement, taking care to not place it over a jewel, pivot, or any of the setting parts. It must be on a flat surface. Place 2-3 of the dial dots on the movement in this manner (Fig. 7).

16. Remove the top paper from the dial dots by pressing the back end of the tweezers onto the dot in a circular motion, until the paper separates from the dot (you will then see the adhesive, like two-sided tape) and remove the paper. (NOTE: NEVER USE SUPERGLUE TO ATTACH A DIAL TO A MOVEMENT!)

17. If it is not already installed on the new movement, place the hour wheel on the canon pinion as above.

18. Place the readied dial back on to the movement, taking care that you have the 3 at the stem side, and that the canon pinion and hour wheel are centered in the hole in the middle of the dial. Press the dial firmly onto the movement.

19. Install the hands as above.

20. Put the movement into the case, set the time and check that the watch is running.

Retrofitting from a Non-Standard Movement Size

Now we will deal with a watch that is either quartz or mechanical for which there is no exact size equivalent available.

Remember the old quartz movement I suggested you put aside for future use with Speedi Fit? Here's where that comes in handy. Let's say we are dealing with a rare, 7 ligne round movement and case and there is no readily available quartz movement of equivalent size available. It makes no difference whether this is a quartz or mechanical, but for the purposes of this chapter, let's say it is an antique ladies' pendant watch. Because there is no exact replacement, we must make a custom fitted movement ring using Speedi Fit (sometimes called Retro-Eze). This is very simple, but can be messy.

1. Take a small amount of Speedi fit (about the size of two peas) from each of the base and catalyst jars. Use *slightly* more catalyst than base. I find this makes a much more rigid result.

2. Quickly mix the two balls together until it is a uniform color. It hardens quite quickly. You have less than 5 minutes to mold the case.

3. Fill the caseback with the mixture.

4. Insert your junk movement into the mixture, centering it as closely as possible to center, with the stem in position.

Then...wait. Don't be in a hurry.

5. Allow the mold to dry thoroughly, about 5 minutes, depending on the ratio of catalyst to base. Check the mold for hardness by poking it with the point of your tweezers. When the tweezers leave no indentation, the mold is dry and you can remove the junk movement.

6. Use your scalpel to trim the excess vinyl (that's what you've just made, a vinyl mold) overflowing the case.

Then follow the above retrofitting instructions.

You will find that as you begin offering your own, in-house quartz watch service, more and more customers will come your way, as well as having other jewelers sending you referrals.

This goes to the root of what this book is meant to provide...
to help you achieve your goals by providing unparalleled,
excellent service far beyond that of your competitors.

By now I hope that you are treating all your repair customers
as the persons they really are – the most important person you
meet in your retail environment on a daily basis.

When we treat our customers as the important persons they
are, something very important happens in their minds.

When we sell the customer a piece of merchandise, he or she
feels that he has done us a favor.
Conversely, in the customer's mind, when we give them
outstanding service, they feel *we* have done *them* a favor.

By offering outstanding service, we are creating a pool of
customer loyalty that is hard to achieve by selling
merchandise. Remember, what repairs we do are important,
worthwhile, and worth every cent we charge.

Order of Illustrations on Following Pages

www.watchfix.com   www.watchrepairbooks.com
www.watchrepairvideos.com   www.watchrepairseminars.com

Detent Button

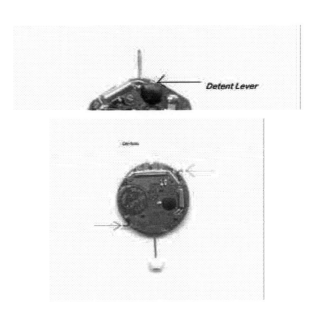

Detent Lever

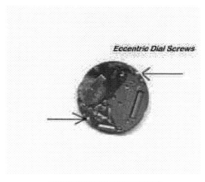

Eccentric Dial Screws

Eccentric Dial Screw

Dial Dots / Strips

Chapter 6

Associations And Resources

Here is a list of organizations and resources that you will find helpful in your watch repair business. Please note that we receive no compensation for any listing here.

Trade Associations can be very valuable to your business, by offering new resources and invaluable information. Additionally, membership can add to your prestige.

www.watchfix.com
www.watchrepairvideos.com
www.watchrepairbooks.com
www.watchrepairseminars.com

138

TRADE ASSOCIATIONS

The National Horological Institute

P.O. Box 37.

Timberon, NM 88350

505-987-2557

Dedicated to education in the watch repair trades as a viable, profitable career.

Polygon Network

P.O. Box 4806

Dillon, CO 80435

800-221-4435

www.polygon.net

This is a private Internet network for retail jewelers, pawnshops, coin dealers and related wholesalers. On this network, diamonds are bought and sold as well as watches. I know of no one who has joined the system who has not found it to be an invaluable resource.

Jewelers Vigilance Committee

25 West 45th St. #400

New York, NY 10036

212-997-2002 800-JOIN-JVC

"The Industry's Guardian of Ethics and Integrity", this organization investigates claims of fraud and misrepresentation within the industry.

Society for Professional Watchmakers

P.O. Box 37

Timberon, NM 88350

505-987-2557

No Membership Fee

The SPW's aim is preservation of watch repair as an economically viable and professional career.

BOOKS

THE COMPLETE PRICE GUIDE TO WATCHES

by Cooksey Shugart

Cooksey Shugart Publications

P.O.Box 3147

Cleveland, TN 37320.

ISBN # 1-57432-064-5

This is the standard price guide for watch collectors and dealers and jewelers worldwide. This book contains 1,080 pages and is published yearly. Contains great information on pricing and pictures on the watches listed, and a biography on every watch manufacturer listed. This book can be bought from your local bookstore or from your watch material resource. It is an indispensable tool for doing appraisals.

Consultants

David Geller

Jeweler Profit

510 Sutters Point N.E.

Atlanta , GA 30328

(404) 255-9565; fax (404) 252-9835

Pricing guidelines for repairs and custom work. Uses a 3-time markup on the finding and a 4-time markup on the jeweler.

Dan Gendron C.M.H.

P.O. Box 37

Timberon, NM 88350

(505) 987-2557 www.watchfix.com

WATCH SUPPLIERS

Inventory Adjusters

3437 E. McDowell Rd.

Phoenix, AZ 85008

602-278-5966

Most major retailers rotate their inventory every 90 to 180 days. This means that they clear their shelves of merchandise that has not sold in that time period, whether the merchandise is still viable or not. Inventory Adjusters is one of the companies that purchases this "close-out" merchandise and passes it on to you for pennies on the dollar. They offer low-end fashion watches at $5 to $10 cost and many higher-end brands such as Seiko, Movado and Omega also at greatly reduced prices.

Serge's & Co.

Chip Hurd

3841 W. Broward Blvd

Plantation, FL 33312

877-973-7437

Deals in quality pre-owned watches.

CRYSTAL FITTERS

Murphy's Crystal Service

1839 N. Central Ave. #B

Ceres, CA 95307

209-531-1738

There are many times when a pre-made crystal cannot be ordered to fit a case. In these cases, knowing a good crystal fitter is essential. When sending a watch to a crystal fitter, the movement must be removed from the case first. Call Rob at Murphy's for some pre-printed envelopes in which to send your bezels.

WATCH REPAIR SERVICES

Clay Minton CMH

P.O. Box 100

Blossom, TX 75416

903-785-8889

AboutTime@1starnet.com

Dan Gendron CMH

P.O. Box 37

Timberon, NM 88350

(505) 987-2557

Chapter 7
Dealing in Vintage Watches

www.watchfix.com   www.watchrepairbooks.com
www.watchrepairvideos.com   www.watchrepairseminars.com

In previous chapters, we have studied repair services and the fundamentals of watch mechanics, both quartz and mechanical. These studies serve as a basis on which to build your watch business as a whole.

The next chapter will discuss dealing in antique, vintage and high-grade wrist and pocket watches.

Dealing in vintage and collectible watches can be very profitable and highly rewarding. This is an area in which you can really stand out in your market area, partly because there is so little competition. But it does require some knowledge on your part to be successful at this.

There are many instances in which those who deal in vintage watches buy a watch for a $1000 in the morning and sell it in the afternoon for $1,500.

Most often, customers who want to sell vintage or antique watches resort to pawn shops for lack of any other local, trusted venue with which to do business. With a little bit of effort on your part, they can become *your* clients, providing you with inventory to attract and cater to the "collector" trade as well as the clientele in your market area who are looking for a "special" watch from time to time.

✓ *The key to being successful when dealing with pre-owned watches is **information**.*

When someone comes in "off the street" with a vintage or high-grade watch to sell you must at least know what resources are available to you to help you evaluate the piece and buy wisely.

This chapter is a primer on the book, *The Complete Price Guide to Watches*. We begin here because it is the starting point for the basic understanding needed for success in this part of the business.

I truly can't fathom anyone dealing in watches on any level (appraisals, buying selling, repairing, etc.), without a copy of *The Complete Price Guide to Watches* by Cooksey Shugart, Tom Engle, and Richard E. Gilbert, ISBN 1-57432-130-7. It is an annual publication and is available from your watch material dealer.

This book is truly an encyclopedia of watches. Hardly a week goes by that I don't get a phone all from a jeweler asking me to help him with an appraisal. *My* resource in that event is this book. But there are a few things to understand before one can take full advantage of this resource. Remember, when using this book that it is a *GUIDE*, not an absolute.

For the purposes of this chapter we refer to Volume 19 of The Complete Price Guide to Watches. Please follow along in that edition:

www.watchfix.com
www.watchrepairvideos.com
www.watchrepairbooks.com
www.watchrepairseminars.com

149

Watch Grading Terminology

In the first chapter is the industry standard and accepted Grading Guidelines for used watches. I am sure if you read over these grading guidelines that you will find that there are many instances in which a watch dealer has mis-graded a watch to you.

The most popular mis-grading is in the use of the term "Pristine Mint". You will notice that the definition of grade "G-10, Pristine-Mint" is "New old stock. Absolutely factory new; sealed in factory box with wax paper still intact and all tags, papers, etc." From this description you probably now know that you may have never seen a "pristine" old watch.

Regrettably, many dealers use this term because it sells, not necessarily because it's true. There are many dealers (particularly on television) who commonly mis-grade this way and even use the term deceitfully. They use the term pristine (or sometimes *"mint-y"*) when in fact the watches usually grade in the G-6 to G-4 category.

It is essential that we as professionals use these guidelines precisely to grade watches.

American Watch Sizes

Also in the first chapter is an explanation of how to determine American movement sizes, with a cross-reference to inches, millimeters and lignes. It is essential when dealing with American watches – wrist or pocket -- that we understand the American movement sizes so that you can find a particular watch in the book.

Hallmarks

When attempting to determine the value of a watch, it is essential to confirm what metal content the case actually has. Look up in the glossary to find the Hallmarks of Solid Gold American watchcases. Prior to the uniform metal stampings act, many watchcases were marked 10, 14, and 18 karat that were only gold-filled. Many other watch cases were marked "Warranted 14 kt gold" that were also only gold filled. The "warranty" in this case was only that the layer of gold over the basemetal was 14 kt.

Also included is the gold-filled and silver case marks. As an example, we see the bell 14kt, 25 years listed in the gold-filled category.

Pocket Watch Nomenclature

Pages 42 and 43 contain the nomenclature of pocket watch parts. As we discussed previously, it is important for you to speak knowledgeably to gain the respect of the clientele you wish to court.

There are many cases in which an American made pocket watch was "private labeled". For example, my great- great-grandfather's jewelry store was in Canada and I own an 18-size watch marked "Gendron Special" on the dial and movement. The Elgin National Watch Co manufactured it in 1891.

www.watchfix.com   www.watchrepairbooks.com
www.watchrepairvideos.com   www.watchrepairseminars.com
152

This practice was rather popular in the late 19th and early 20th century. In these cases we can refer to balance cock identifer section ,then we can determine the balance cock and regulator to its corresponding manufacturer. There are many cases when you will be examining an American pocket watch and this will be the only way to determine the manufacturer of origin.

The handy book contains a legend, that is abbreviations and descriptions used throughout the book. When using this book, it is important to refer back to this page whenever you read something in a description of a watch that you don't quite understand.

American Pocket Watch Manufacturers

The first listings in the book are divided alphabetically by the names of American pocket watch manufacturers.

Turn with me now to the American Waltham Watch Co. Under the listing for each manufacturer you will find a short biography of the company.

Following that is a list of serial numbers and the cross-reference to their year of manufacture. This refers to the serial number found on the movement, not on the case. This is how we determine the "circa" date (approximate date of manufacture) of the watch.

Following the serial numbers is a list of all of the most commonly found models in descending order, by size.

Crescent St., 15 J, M#1870, KW – AVG $150   EX-FN $200 MINT $400

This listing describes an 18 size, 15 jewel, Waltham Crescent St., Keywind, Model 1870. In average condition it would be valued at $150, in extra-fine condition $200 and in mint condition $400.

European Pocket Watches

London and Swiss Hallmarks. These are used to determine the "circa" date of many European watches. On the inside of the caseback there will be a hallmark with a letter within a shield. These letters correspond to a year in these listings.

European pocket watch manufacturers. It is laid out identically to the American pocket watch section.

Wristwatch Listings

You will notice that the wristwatch listings show the complete watch, but are somewhat more abbreviated than the pocket watches. It would take volumes to list every wristwatch made. Because of this, the more common models of each manufacturer are listed.

There will be many instances in which it will be necessary to find a similar watch to use for comparison for a watch you may be trying to evaluate. For example Elgin wristwatch in 14-kt gold. If you have an Elgin wristwatch in 14-kt gold that is very similar to a watch you find in the Elgin listings but slightly different, you can use the watch pictured as a guide to value it.

Take Action

✓ Get and keep an up-to-date edition of
   The Complete Price Guide to Watches

✓ Become familiar with the book so that you can easily and confidently use it to evaluate watches that will be brought to you "off the street" to buy.

Chapter 8
Watch Manufacturer
Identification and
Reference Guide

Mechanical Movement Identification Through the Bestfit Material System

Many of you may question why this topic is important. We realize many of you have in-house watchmakers or watchmakers to whom you send your watches for repair. But I can't tell you how many times I receive phone calls from otherwise very knowledgeable watch repairmen who do not understand completely how to order parts. There are many times a repairman will return a watch stating that there are no parts available, when it was only a case of they didn't know what the movement originally was, or how to get parts.

This chapter will give you the capability to speak the same language as the parts supply houses and even help your own watchmaker, and your self.

This chapter is almost esoteric, that is it will explain the mystery of how watch repairpersons figure out what is the model (caliber), or make of an unknown movement, as well as what it cross references to.

The book we in the trade use for this purpose is the **_Bestfit 111 Encyclopedia of Watch Material._** This book is universally used by those in the trade and those who supply parts, if you cannot find a copy of this book new, try looking on Ebay for a used one.

European Watch Movements

The easiest way to identify the caliber of a movement is if there is a visible Hallmark on the movement. This is not always the same name that is on the dial. Actually, most of the time it will be different.

Located on page 3 through page 5 are the Hallmarks of most Swiss and other European movements. You will notice that many times the design of the Hallmark has no relationship to the name of the manufacturer. For example, the Valjoux movement's Hallmark is a shield and the letter R.

The Hallmark is most often stamped into the metal plate under the balance wheel. The makers of most Swiss movements identify their movements this way.

When looking for the Hallmark, also look for a number stamped upon the movement as well, which can be found stamped into the movement under the balance, or stamped onto the train bridge, or on the dial side of the movement. If there is a Hallmark and number, identification is that much easier, but that will not always be the case. If both are present, we can go directly to the section of the book that covers that type of movement.

If there is neither a Hallmark nor a number visible (sometimes the OEM will have milled off these identifiers), we can use the size of the movement (measured in lignes) to begin to identify it.

If you don't have a ligne gauge, get one. They are very inexpensive and will have American measurements on the back as well. Measure the diameter of the movement if it is a round movement. If it is any other shape, measure the two widest points (width and length) of the movement. A very popular, non-round movement size is 6 ¾ X 8 lignes.

Like with the Quartz Movements Catalog, we must pay attention to the features of the movement. Also located on page 5 are the abbreviation codes for the features of the movements. There are alarms, chronographs, calendars etc.

Pages 9 through 11 are a "dictionary" listing of all typical watch parts.

Page 14 begins the alphabetical listing of watch movements. Lets assume that you have found an Admiral Hallmark under the balance wheel of a 13-ligne movement. The first listing on page 14 is Admiral 13 Ligne. You will notice that there is no listing for the calibre. This is because we determine the model of this particular movement by its ligne size, in this case, 13 lignes.

We also see that the "Movement Interchangeability" (what the movement *originally* was) is a "Tav" (Tavannes) model 370. If you then look in the alphabetical listings under Tavannes, the Tavannes calibre 370 and its part numbers are listed on page 107. This is the cross-conversion.

The Illustration for the Tavannes 370 is on page 145. This is how we confirm that the movement we are trying to identify is truly a Tavannes 370.

If you look at page 145, there is first of all a circle which, if you place the movement on it, will act as a gauge. You will then see a series of boxes, each one with the uniquely shaped setting parts for the movement noted in that box.

In the box marked Tavannes 370, you will see a picture of the three setting parts -- the yoke bridge, detent, and clutch lever. If we take the dial off this movement we will see the setting parts, and if the shapes of those parts match up we have identified that movement.

Now let's go back to page 14 and define the columns seen throughout the alphabetical listings.

- Calibre -- The Calibre is the model number of a movement. If there is one stamped on the movement, it would be either stamped on one of the bridge plates or under the dial on the dial side of the movement (you will have to remove the dial to see it), or, more commonly, stamped into the plate under the balance wheel.

- Lignes -- This is the diameter of the movement in lignes measurement in the case of a round movement. In the case of a movement of another shape than round, you measure the widest part of the width of the movement and the widest part of the length of the movement.

- Movement Interchangeability – this is what the movement *originally* was, regardless of the brand name on the dial or movement. So when moving on to the illustration page number, you will be looking for the name listed in this column. That is, even though the easily visible hallmark on the movement was "Admiral", you will be looking for the illustrations for Tavannes.

- Movement Identification Details -- Listed on page 5 are the movement identification details abbreviation codes. This lists everything from alarm to timer and everything in between. As was the case is the quartz movement catalog, it is important to note features such as, alarm, calendar, etc.

The next columns show the Bestfit System part numbers for the most commonly replaced parts of the movement.

- Staff listing - The Bestfit prefix for balance staffs is 100, therefore the Tavannes balance staff Bestfit part number is 100-241. You will notice that there is a listing for staff and an incabloc staff. An incabloc balance staff is one that has a shock jewel. This is easy to notice because the incabloc balance has a brass spring above the balance jewel.

- Stem – Bestfit prefix 200: This is the Bestfit part number for the stem for this watch, e.g., 200-797F

- Waterproof Stem -- Bestfit prefix 360: Although there is none listed here, this category is for watches that would have a 2-piece stem.

- Pallet Arbor – Bestfit prefix 72S: This is for the pivot on a pallet fork, e.g., 72S-180P

www.watchfix.com
www.watchrepairvideos.com
www.watchrepairbooks.com
www.watchrepairseminars.com

164

- Roller Table with Jewel – Prefix 82S: First listing is non-incabloc, second listing is incabloc, e.g., 82S-143R for non-incabloc.

- Balance Complete – Bestfit prefix 721: This includes balance wheel, hairspring, roller table and balance staff. E.g. 721-673.

- Hands – Bestfit prefix 66S : This includes hour and minute hands only, e.g., 66S-82H

- Second hand -- prefix 66S2ND: denotes the second hand, e.g., 66S2ND-79H

- White-A-Loy MSPG – this is the white alloy mainspring number, no prefix.

- MSPG – Dennison: this denotes the actual measurements of the mainspring, no prefix. The numbers in this column are the width (in mainspring gauge terms), strength (thickness in mainspring gauge terms), and length (in inches). In order to use this identification method you will need a mainspring gauge.

- Samson MSPG: This is an old mainspring system in which the mainsprings are made from blue steel rather than white-alloy metal. This system hasn't been made for 50 years, but some of you may actually have an old system hanging around your store. If you do, the number listed here corresponds to the number on the envelope in the Samson system and you can identify on which movements they can be used.

Other watch companies not covered in the Bestfit book:

Audemars Piguet -- On the movement bridge will be the watch calibre, and on the inside case back will be the case number for casing parts.

Baume & Mercier -- On the movement bridge will be the calibre, and on the outside case back for casing parts

Bulova, Caravelle: They mark their movements with a calibre number. The first one or two digits denote the ligne size of the movement, e.g., in a 5BC movement the number 5 means 5 lignes, the other letters are the internal features of the movement. For case parts on these watches that are very old there is a number on the inside back of the case, such as C8101.

Cartier -- On the movement bridge there will be a calibre, and on the inside and outside case back will be the case number.

Citizen: This is also a number located on the outer back of these watches. Similar to Seiko but there is four digit number for the movement and a 5 digit number for the case. Other than that everything else is the same as Seiko.

Ebel -- On the movement will be a calibre. Look closely... there maybe an ETA number also. On the inside case back will be the number for case parts

Eterna -- On the movement there will be listed the calibre and an EB number and on the inside case back for case number.

Gucci -- On the movement will be the ESA/ETA number and on the inside case back for the case number.

IWC (International Watch Co.) -- On the movement there will be a calibre and EB number and on the inside case back for case number.

Jaeger Lecoutre -- On the movement bridge will be the calibre. On the inside case back will be the case number.

Longines Wittnauer -- On the movement there will be a calibre and an EB number, and on the inside case back will be the case number.

Mido -- Located on the movement bridge and under the balance will be the calibre for ordering movement parts and for casing parts there is a number on the inside case back.

Movado, Zenith -- On the movement will be a calibre and an EB number. On the inside case back is the case number.

www.watchfix.com
www.watchrepairvideos.com
www.watchrepairbooks.com
www.watchrepairseminars.com

168

Omega, Tissot -- On the movement bridge there will be a number, e.g., 570. This is the movement number. Use this to order all movement parts. For case parts, on the inside case back there will a number such as 1020-10003. Use the number found there to order casing parts.

Patek Phillipe -- Located on the movement bridge will be a calibre, and on the inside case back will be a case number e.g., 5250 for casing parts.

Raymond Weil -- On the movement will be the calibre and on the inside case back for the case number.

Rolex, Tudor -- Located on the movement bridge will be a number, e.g., 3135. The number found there would be the number used for ordering movement parts. For casing parts there is a number such as 16000 in the inside case back and between the lugs at the 6 o'clock side.

Seiko, Pulsar, Lorus, Sharp --This company uses an 8 digit number on the outside back of the case, e.g., 8122-5279. The first four digits denote the movement caliber. When ordering movement parts (stems, coils, circuits, or any internal movement parts) this is the part of the number used. You will also find it marked on the movement as well. For casing parts (crystals, crowns, etc.) the complete number is used along with the color of the case. For dials we use the number located on the dial below the number6, it may be necessary to remove the movement from the case to find this number. For watchbands we use the case number and the band number, usually found on the end of the band nearest the case lug.

Swiss Army, Wenger -- On the movement will be the EB number and on the outside case back will be the case number.

Tag-Heuer -- On the movement will be an E. Baush (EB) number, e.g., ESA 955.112. For casing parts there will be a number on the outside case back.

Timex -- The identifying number on a Timex watch will be found on the dial below the number 6. The first two numbers denote the model of the movement, the next four or five number's denote the model of the watch, and the last two denote the year the watch was made.

Vacheron et Constantin -- On the movement will be the calibre and on the inside case back the case number

American Manufacturers

(Elgin, Waltham, Hamilton, Illinois, South Bend, Rockford, etc.)

On the obverse side of your ligne gauge you will find American Watch sizes. American watches never standardized their parts listings. The way we determine the model and calibre is by the size of the movement and its serial number.

There are books that will specify the exact model of movement for a specific serial number but you have no need of these books. Most good material houses are happy to supply parts for American movements based on size and serial number only.

When ordering balance staffs for American watches, we need to know if the roller table is single or double roller. This is easy to identify. If you remove the balance and turn it over, the single roller is a single, flat disk with a roller jewel attached. The double roller is two disks, one with a jewel and one approximately ½ the diameter directly underneath it.

This is the very information we use in our trade shop for watch parts of all types. We hope you find it practical and can put it to use.

Now following is a list of which manufacturers make what modern brands, and their contact information.

MANUFACTURER'S ADDRESSES

ACCUTRON

One Bulova Avenue

Woodside, NY 11377

800-228-5682

718-204-3300; fax 718-204-3414

ADVANCE WATCH CO. LTD.

25800 Sherwood

Warren, MI 48091

800 477-4788 / 810 755-3000 fax: 810-755-4531

AERO

Exclusive Time International

765 Mountain Ave., Suite 316

Springfield, NJ 07081

973-376-8667; fax 973-912-9723

ALFEX OF SWITZERLAND

Swiss Watch Corp.

14 E. 38th St., Second Floor

New York, NY 10016

800-237-9477

212-696-1881; fax 212-213-5494

ALFRED DUNHILL

100 Niantic Ave.

Providence, RI 02907

401-943-4230; fax 401-943-4230

service: 800-551-1351; other 800-556-7354

AMERICAN PD COMPANY

12700 Yukon Ave.

Hawthorne, CA 90250

310-644-5841; fax 310-644-4210

ANDRE FLEURY

SWISS WATCH CORP.

523 Fourth St.

San Rafael, CA 94901

415-459-7755; fax 415-459-0724

ANNE KLEIN

29-10 Thomson Avenue

Long Island City, NY 11101

800-937-0050

718-784-0700; fax 718-786-2120

ARISTO IMPORT CO., INC.

15 Hunt Rd.

Orangeburg, NY 10962

845-359-0720; fax 845-359-0020

ARMITRON

29-10 Thomson Ave.

Long Island City, NY 11101

800-937-0050; 718-784-2120; fax 718-482-2700

A. T. CROSS CO.

One Albion Rd.

Lincoln, RI 02865

800-452-9312

401-333-1200; fax 401-334-4590

AUDEMARS PIGUET

Time Products Inc.

545 Madison Ave., 13th floor

New York, NY 10022

212-758-8400; fax 212-758-8538

AUGUSTE REYMOND

2013 Colorado Blvd. "A"

Denton, TX 76205

940-484-4976; fax 817-430-9868

AUSTERN & PAUL/
ORGEL - SHORR, INC.

18 E.48th St.

New York NY 10017

800-221-2066

212-753-1717; fax 212-753-2477

BAUME & MERCIER INC.

663 Fifth Ave.

New York, NY 10022-5039

800-582-1337

212-593-0444; fax 212-755-3138

BELAIR TIME CORP.

1995 Swarthmore Ave.

Lakewood, NJ 08701

800-223-1654

732-905-0100; fax 732-367-3215

BELL & ROSS

1688 Meridian Ave., Suite 504

Miami Beach, FL 33139

888-307-7887

305-674-9464; fax 305-672-3840

BENOIR DESIGN LTD.

64 W 48th St.

New York, NY 10036

212 382 0030 Fax 212-382-0054

BERTOLUCCI

Swiss Primetime Inc.

201 Route 17 North

Rutherford, NJ 07070

877-237-8658

201-804-1902; fax 201-804-1898

BLANCPAIN

See: The Swatch Group

BONNEVILLE WATCHES

3544 E. Enterprise Dr.

Anaheim, CA 92807

888-999-7258

714-666-1999; fax 714-666-1955

BREGUET LLC

444 Madison Ave., Suite 601

New York, NY 10022

888-273-4838

212-688-4500; fax 212-888-5025

BULGARI CORP. OF AMERICA

730 Fifth Ave.

New York, NY 10019

800-644-4636

212-315-9000; fax 212-541-8060

BULOVA CORP.

One Bulova Ave.

Woodside, NY 11377

800-228-5682

718-204-3300; fax 718-204-3546

BURETT SWISS
SPORTS WATCHES

40 Seaview Dr.

Secaucus, NJ 07094

888-828-7388;

201-902-0347; fax 201-902-9342

CALVIN KLEIN

See: The Swatch Group

CARRERA Y CARRERA, INC.

33 Riverside Ave.

Westport, CT 06880

800-292-8229; fax 203-227-8923

CARTIER INC.

653 Fifth Ave.

New York, NY 10022

212-753-0111; fax 212-826-6956

CASIO

570 Mt. Pleasant Ave

Dover, NJ 07801

973-361-5400; fax 973-361-3819

CHANEL INC.

15 East 57th St.

New York, NY 10022

212-715-4100; fax 212-715-4158

CHASE-DURER

270 N. Canon Drive #1402

Beverly Hills, CA 90210

310-550-7280; fax 310-550-0830

CHAUMET

960 S. Springfield Ave.

Springfield, NJ 07081

800-321-4832

973-467-1890; fax 973-467-8938

CHOPARD WATCH CORP.

630 Fifth Ave., Ste. 3225

New York, NY 10111

800-246-7273

212-218-7218; fax 212-218-7228

CHRISTIAN DIOR WATCHES

960 S. Springfield Ave.

Springfield, NJ 07081

800-321-4832

973-467-1890; fax 973-467-8938

www.watchfix.com
www.watchrepairvideos.com
www.watchrepairbooks.com
www.watchrepairseminars.com

182

**CITIZEN WATCH COMPANY OF
AMERICA, INC**
1200 Wall St. West
Lyndhurst, NJ 07071
201-438-8150; fax 201-438-4161

**COLEMAX
INTERNATIONAL, INC.**
135 W. 29th St., 3rd Floor
New York, NY 10001
800-713-6337
212-244-2010; fax 212-244-1729

COLIBRI
100 Niantic Ave.
Providence, RI 02907
800-556-7354
401-943-2100; fax 401-943-4230

www.watchfix.com   www.watchrepairbooks.com
www.watchrepairvideos.com   www.watchrepairseminars.com
183

CONCORD WATCH CO.

Wes KettleKamp Company

4708 W. 84th St.

Bloomington, MN 55437

952-831-4406; fax 952-832-0575

CORUM

Corum USA, LLC

3 Mason

Irvine, CA 92618

949-458-4200; fax 949-458-1258

CROTON WATCH Co. INC

NATIONWIDE TIME INC.

15 W. 37th St.

New York, NY 10018

800-443-7639

212-764-5858; fax 212-764-6175

www.watchfix.com
www.watchrepairvideos.com
www.watchrepairbooks.com
www.watchrepairseminars.com

184

CYMA WATCH

GLENN CORP.

350 Fifth Ave., #1308

New York, NY 10118

212-695-4270; fax 212-695-4284

DANIEL MINK

The Montreux Group

560 Main St., Suite 2A

Allenhurst, NJ 07711

800-221-6465

732-663-9550; fax 732-663-9552

DANIEL ROTH

Walter Gooden, Inc.

2050 Bundy Drive, Suite 290

Los Angeles, CA 90025

310-820-5952; fax 310-820-3594

DAVID YURMAN

501 Madison Ave.

New York, NY 10022

212-593-1122; fax 212-593-1597

DUNDEE

Division of OSI Chicago, Inc.

2929 N. California Avenue

Chicago, IL 60618

800-235-9727

773-583-5203; fax 773-583-8110

EBEL USA, INC.

750 Lexington Ave., 10th Floor

New York, NY 10022

212-888-EBEL; fax 212-980-5630

ECCLISSI

7 W. 36th St.

New York, NY10018

800-358-8039

212-967-5666; fax 212-695-0706

EGANA OF SWITZERLAND (AMERICA) CORP.

Parsec Enterprises

7501 N. Harker Drive

P.O. Box 195

Peoria, IL 61650-0195

800-359-2508

309-689-6531; fax 309-689-2508

ETA

See: The Swatch Group

FALCON WATCH CO.

1972 Ridge Lake Drive

Chesterfield, MO 63017

800-506-8222

636-532-8220; fax 636-532-8222

www.watchfix.com
www.watchrepairvideos.com
www.watchrepairbooks.com
www.watchrepairseminars.com

187

FENDI

Taramax USA, Inc.

600 Warren Ave.

Spring Lake Heights, NJ 07762

732-282-0300; fax 732-282-0404

FESTINA USA INC.

121 West Nyack Road, Suite 13

PO. Box 638

Nanuet, NY 10954

845-623-8525; fax 845-623-8224

FLIK FLAK

See: The Swatch Group

FOSSIL, INC.

2280 N. Greenville Ave.

Richardson, TX 75082

800-842-8621

972-234-2525; fax 972-234-4669

FRANCK MULLER USA INC.

207 W. 25th St., 8th Floor

New York, NY 10001

800-772-8788

212-463-8898; fax 212-463-7082

GENENDER INTERNATIONAL

390 Fifth Ave.

New York, NY 10018

212-643-0440; fax 212-643-0999

GERALD GENTA

Walter Gooden, Inc.

2050 Bundy Drive, Suite 290

Los Angeles, CA 90025

310-820-5952; fax 310-820-3594

GIRARD-PERREGAUX

Tradema of America

201 Route 17 North

Rutherford, NJ 07070

877-846-3447

201-804-1904; fax 201-804-1898

www.watchfix.com
www.watchrepairvideos.com
www.watchrepairbooks.com
www.watchrepairseminars.com

189

GUCCI TIMEPIECES

625 Madison Ave., 11th Floor

New York, NY 10022

212-527-5400; fax 212-527-5433

HAMILTON

See: The Swatch Group

HARRY WINSTON, INC.

718 Fifth Ave.

NewYork, NY 10019

212-245-2000; fax 212-315-0818

THE HERMES WATCH CO.

745 Fifth Avenue, Suite 2010

New York, NY 10151

212-835-6562; fax 212-835-6560

www.watchfix.com
www.watchrepairvideos.com
www.watchrepairbooks.com
www.watchrepairseminars.com

190

HUBLOT

MDM of America Inc.

The International Building

2451 E. Sunrise Blvd., Suite ST4

Fort Lauderdale, FL 33304

800-536-0636

954-568-9400; 954-568-0636

IKEPOD, LLC

444 Madison Avenue, Suite 601

New York, NY 10022

212-688-4500; fax 212-888-5025

IWC

P.O. Box 1807

188 Brooke Rd.

Winchester, VA 22603

800-432-9330

540-665-0474; fax 540-665-4130

JAEGER-LECOULRE

845 Third Avenue, 19th Floor

New York, NY 10022

800-552-4230

212-308-2525; 212-308-0614

JAGUAR

See Festina USA

JEAN MARCEL LLC

1200 N. Federal Highway, Suite 200

Boca Raton, FL 33432

561-558-9557; fax 561-558-9558

JOHN HARDY COLLECTION

14 E. 38th St.

New York, NY 10016

800-237-9577

212-696-1881; fax 212-213-5494

JULES JURGENSEN

101 W. City Ave.

Bala Cynwyd, PA 19004

800-220-1233

610-667-3500; fax 610-667-3522

JUNGHANS

LaCrosse McCormick

1116 South Oak Street

La Crescent, MN 55947

800-346-9544

507-895-1000; fax 507-895-8000

JUVENIA USA

62 W. 47th St., Room 304

New York, NY 10036

800-431-6683

212-719-2710; fax 212-575-3069

www.watchfix.com
www.watchrepairvideos.com
www.watchrepairbooks.com
www.watchrepairseminars.com

193

KELEK SWISS WATCH

155 Harbor Dr., #1008

Chicago, IL 60601

888-860-0540

312-861-0682; fax 312-861-0645

KRIEGER WATCH CO.

300 71st St. Suite 640

Miami Beach, FL 33141

800-441-8433

305-861-1804; fax 305-861-1807

LA MARQUE WATCH CO.

306 Hempstead Ave.

Malverne, NY 11565

800-247-7788

516-887-4700; fax 516-599-8818

LASSALE®

See: Seiko Corporation of America

www.watchfix.com
www.watchrepairvideos.com
www.watchrepairbooks.com
www.watchrepairseminars.com

194

LEVI'S

See: Genender Intl.

LINDEN

100 Niantic Ave.

Providence, RI 02907

401-943-2100; fax 401-943-4230

LONGINES

See: The Swatch Group

LORUS

The King Company

1309 Ruthetford Lane, #160

Austin, TX 78753

800-443-3617

512-349-3800; fax 512-349-3000

LUCIEN PICCARD

876 62nd St.

Brooklyn, NY 11220

718-491-8604; fax 718-491-8607

MAJESTIME

Majesti Watch Co.

70 W. 36th St.

New York, NY 10018

212-239-0444; fax 212-629-4371

MARCEL WATCH CO.

200 Meadowlands Pkwy.

Secaucus, NJ 07094-2302

800-422-6053

201-330-5600; fax 201-330-0218

MAURICE LACROIX U.S.A.

17835 Ventura Blvd., #301

Encino, CA 91316

800-794-7736

818-609-8686; fax 818-609-7079

MDM OF AMERICA INC.

The International Bldg., Suite ST4

2451 East Sunrise Blvd.

Ft. Lauderdale, FL 33304

800-536-0636

954-568-9400; fax 954-568-6337

MEDANA WATCH CORP.

44 E. 32nd St.

New York, NY 10016

800-289-8963

212-889-3560; fax 212-213-2649

MICHAEL ANTHONY JEWELERS, INC.

115 5. MacQuesten Pkwy.

Mt. Vernon, NY 10550-1724

800-966-8800

914-699-0000; fax 914-699-9614

MICHEL HERBELIN
1000 Lincoln Rd., Ste. 210
Miami Beach, FL 33139
800-725-7047
305-532-2717; fax 305-532-2571

MICHEL JORDI
US MJD, Inc.
4230 L.B.J. Freeway #404
Dallas, TX 75244
800-823-8340
972-960-0335; fax 972-788-4644

MICHELE WATCH CO.
20201 Northeast 16th Place
Miami, FL 33179
800-522-8463
305-650-9771; fax 305-650-9729

www.watchfix.com
www.watchrepairvideos.com
www.watchrepairbooks.com
www.watchrepairseminars.com
198

MINERVA INTRO-SWISS

1775 Forest Ave.

Boulder, CO 80304

303-440-0675; fax 303-443-3563

MOMO DESIGN

3138 Commadore Plaza, Suite 318

Miami, FL 33133

305-461-3585; fax 305-461-2331

MONTBLANC

26 Main St., 3rd Floor

Chatham, NJ 07928

973-665-7200; 973-635-0157

MOVADO

Movado Group, Inc.

125 Chubb Ave.

Lyndhurst, NJ 07071

201-518-7100; fax 201-460-3832

NOBEL WATCH CO.

32 Broadway, 18th Floor

New York, NY 10004

800-662-3595

212-785-2040; fax 212-785-2042

OMEGA

See: The Swatch Group

ORIS USA INC.

2 Skyline Dr.

Hawthorne, NY 10532

914-347-6747; fax 914-347-4782

PATEK PHILIPPE

Dist. by Henri Stern Agency Inc.

1 Rockefeller Plaza #930

New York, NY 10020

212-218-1240; fax 212-218-1255

PAUL PICOT OF AMERICA INC

6227 Constitution Drive

Fort Wayne, IN 46804

800-887-2717

260-436-4563; fax 260-436-4564

PERRY ELLIS

See: Genender Intl., Inc.

PHILIPPE CHARRIOL U.S.A.

1227 Prospect St.

La Jolla, CA 92037

800-872-2567

858-454-0011; fax 858-454-9944

PIAGET

See: Movado Group, Inc.

PORSCHE

See: American PD Company

RADO

See: The Swatch Group

RAYMOND WEIL

Seville Watch Co.

587 Fifth Ave.

New York, NY 10017

212-355-3350; fax 212-355-3720

REUGE MUSIC USA LTD.

5741 Buckingham Pkwy., Unit B

Culver City, CA 90230

310-410-7040; fax 310-410-0792

REVUE THOMMEN

765 Mountain Ave., Suite 316

Springfield, NJ 07081

973-376-8667; fax 973-912-9723

www.watchfix.com
www.watchrepairvideos.com
www.watchrepairbooks.com
www.watchrepairseminars.com

202

ROLEX WATCH USA, INC.

665 Fifth Ave.

New York, NY 10022-5383

212-758-7700; fax 212-371-0371

ROTARY WATCHES

(USA) INC.

9030 Leslie St., Suite 1

Richmond Hill, Ontario, Canada L4B 1G2

905-764-2133; fax 905-764-0457

ROVEN DINO TIMEPIECES

American Precision Watch

30 Chapin Rd., #1208

P.O. Box 611

Pinebrook, NJ 07058

800-882-8608

973-882-6636; fax 973-882-6463

**SAINT-HONORE WATCH
CORPORATION**
107-06 71st Rd., 2nd Fl.
Forest Hills, NY 11375
718-793-2740; fax 718-793-8228

SARCAR
Jean Louis Roehrich Inc.
608 5th Ave., Suite 910
New York, NY 10020
212-246-3978; fax 212-765-7476

SECTOR SPORT WATCHES
444 Madison Ave., Suite 601
New York, NY 10022
212-688-4500; fax 212-888-5025

SEIKO CORP OF AMERICA
1111 Macarthur Blvd.
Mahwah, NJ 07430
800-782-2510
201-529-5730; fax 201-529-5985

www.watchfix.com   www.watchrepairbooks.com
www.watchrepairvideos.com   www.watchrepairseminars.com
204

SELCO CUSTOM TIME CORP.

8909 E. 21st St.

Tulsa, OK 74129

800-94-SELCO

918-622-6100; fax 918-622-6729

SKAGEN

7525 Colbert Drive, Suite 108

Reno, NV 89511

800-937-3576

775-850-5500; fax 775-850-5530

THE SWATCH GROUP

1200 Harbor Blvd.

Weehawken, NJ 07087

800-897-9477

201-271-1400; fax 201-271-4633

SWISS ARMY BRANDS, LTD.

One Research Dr

Shelton CT 06484

800 243-4032

203 929 6391;   fax 203-925-1092

TAG HEUER USA

960 S. Springfield Ave.

Springfield, NJ 07081

800-321-4832

973-467-1890; fax 973-467-8938

TECHTIME CORP.

110 Corporate Park Drive

White Plains, NY 10604

914-694-6205 (phone and fax)

TIFFANY & COMPANY

727 Fifth Ave.

New York, NY 10022

212-605-4561; fax 212-605-4465

TIMEX CORP

P. 0. Box 310

Middlebury, CT 06762-0310

800-448-4639

203-573-5000; fax 203-573-5143

TISSOT

See: The Swatch Group

ULYSSE NARDIN

6001 Broken Sound Parkway, Suite 504

Boca Raton, FL 33487

561-988-8600; fax 561-988-0123

VACHERON CONSTANTIN

20 W. 55th St., 12th Fl.

New York, NY 10019

212-713-0707; fax 212-713-0735

VALDAWN INC.

Parsec Enterprises

7501 N. Harker Drive

P.O. Box 195

Peoria, IL 61650-0195

800-359-2508

309-689-6531; fax 309-689-6543

VAN CLEEF & ARPELS

744 Fifth Ave., 2nd Floor

New York, NY 10019

212-644-9500; fax 212-752-9114

VISAGE WATCHES

3 W. 35th St., Mezzanine

New York, NY 10001

800-992-0305

212-967-3344; fax 212-967-3318

WENGER

Wenger North America

15 Corporate Drive

Orangeburg, NY 10962

800-431-2996

845-365-3500; fax 845-425-4700

WITTNAUER

145 Huguenot St.

New Rochelle, NY 10802

800-431-1863

914 654-7200; fax 914 654-7219

XEMEX

Time Central

620 Congress Ave., Suite 208

Austin, Texas 78701

512-499-0123; fax 512-499-8112

All Registered Trademarks are the property of their respective
owners.

Chapter 9
Crystal Clear

other categories. If you can't readily find the fancy shaped crystal you are looking for, look here.

- CH – These are hexagonal crystals. All the edges are straight lines, not rounded, on these crystals.
- CN – These are octagonal, straight edged crystals.
- CO – Oval crystals
- CQ – square crystals with cut corners, with straight edges
- CR – Rectangular crystals with cut corners, with straight edges.
- CS – Square crystals, straight edges
- CT – Rectangular crystals, two sides straight edged, two sides curved edges
- CW – rectangular crystal, all sides curved
- C X – rectangular, all edges straight.
- CY – Cushion shaped, rectangular, all sides curved, less curvature than CW

CYLINDER crystals are mostly used on older, curved bezel watches. An older Gruen Cruvex takes this type of crystal. The base and top of this crystal is curved to conform to the curvature of the case.

The designations for the cylinder crystals are the same as the shapes above, except that they will also contain the letter "M" in the second position, e.g., C M X will be the same as a C X, but the base and top of the crystal will be curved.

Crystal Diagrams in the G-S Catalog

Beginning on page 2 is actual-sized diagrams of crystals. On many of these diagrams, manufacturers using that crystal type are listed and even some case numbers for those manufacturers are listed.

Also listed are the dimensions of each crystal in millimeters, at the two widest points of length and width. (NOTE: Measurements should be taken of the inner ledge of the bezel and not the old crystal.)

Mineral Glass Crystals

Mineral Glass (MG) is a very hard tempered mineral substance from which crystals are often made, particularly on quartz watches. They are measured in tenths of millimeters.

Glass Crystal Types –

- MG – This denotes a round, flat crystal made of mineral glass
- MG Domed – a round, slightly domed, mineral crystal
- MG Thick – this type is used on many diver's models
- MG Painted – this will have a gold ring with black numerals or a black ring with gold numerals painted on the underside of the crystal. These are available in domed and flat.
- Prism Crystals -- Prism crystals are mineral glass crystals that are cut and shaped like a prism, mostly used on Fossil-type watches.

Tools Needed

Glues -

Hypo Cement, a.k.a. Rocket Cement

> This glue is used for plastic crystals only. It is placed on the inside ledge of the case, *VERY SPARINGLY!* Never squeeze the tube. The glue will come out by gravity when held vertically, point down. There should be only a sheen of glue on the ledge, do not fill the ledge with glue.

UV Glue

This glue is ONLY used on glass crystals. It is necessary, however, to have either a UV lamp or direct sunlight for this type of glue to harden. As with the GS glue, use sparingly. Apply with a toothpick to the bezel so that the ledge is only damp with glue. You should not see clumps of glue anywhere.

Note: Never use epoxy or Crazy Glue to glue in a crystal. It is too difficult to remove bits of glass and these dried glues from the ledge of the bezel.

CRYSTAL VICE OR CRYSTAL LIFT

This type of tool is only used on round, friction fitted crystals such as PHD, PKH, etc. To use the vice, hold it teeth up. The crystal is placed into the jaws of the vice upside down with the ledge sticking out of the jaws. Tighten the vice to compress the crystal slightly. The crystal is then placed into the bezel and the jaws are released, allowing the crystal to expand into the bezel for a snug fit.

CRYSTAL FILE OR EMERY BOARD

There will be times when an exact sized crystal is not available. In this case, you can most likely find a similarly shaped, but slightly larger crystal. File the sides until the crystal fits. When filing a crystal, file in long, continuous motions *in one direction only*, remove the file and repeat. Be careful, a little filing takes off quite a bit of crystal.

GS CRYSTAL GAUGE

On page 119 of the G-S catalog, bottom left hand corner, is a picture of a G-S crystal gauge. You will notice it has two sides. As it is shown, the bottom part of this gauge measures GS round crystals. Round crystals are not measured in millimeters, but according to this gauge measurement. The opposite side measures millimeters.

Removing the Old Crystal, Installing the New

Friction crystals (e.g., round plastic, domed, PHD, etc.) -- Place the crystal vice over the crystal so that it rests on the bezel. Tighten the crystal vice onto the crystal and at the same time, slightly twist the crystal until it is loose enough to

www.watchfix.com
www.watchrepairvideos.com
www.watchrepairbooks.com
www.watchrepairseminars.com

217

move within the bezel. Once it is loose enough to move, you will be able to pull it off the bezel using the vice. To put the new crystal on, reverse the order.

Glued Plastic Crystals – In the case of plastic crystals, remove the caseback and the movement. Then push the old crystal out from the inside of the watchcase. Using a small blade (like a screwdriver), scrape away any remaining glue, dirt, pieces of crystal, etc. If there is a lot of remaining glue, etc., you may put the case into the ultrasonic to help clean it out. To install the new crystal, use a SPARING amount of GS crystal cement or Rocket glue, and install the new crystal.

Glued Glass Crystals – In the case of some mineral glass type crystals, you will find the old crystal quite difficult to remove, because the crystal is epoxy-ed onto the watch. In this case, here is a little trick…Use a hairdryer to heat the crystal and the bezel to loosen the epoxy, making it easier to remove. Use UV glue to install the new crystal. Again, use a *sparse* amount of glue, only dampening the bezel with glue.

Friction Gasket Crystals – These are crystals that are held into the watch bezel by means of a white gasket into which the

www.watchfix.com
www.watchrepairvideos.com
www.watchrepairbooks.com
www.watchrepairseminars.com

218

crystal is held by friction. These can be very tricky. Often the gasket is not even necessary. In the case of specific brands, e.g. Tag-Heuer, Breitling, etc., if you are going to replace the old crystal with an original one, be sure to order a new crystal gasket as well. If you are not ordering an original crystal, but rather choosing a crystal based on the measurement of the bezel, you do not usually need the gasket (especially with cheaper watches), but glue the crystal onto the bezel.

Venturing into crystal replacement can be very profitable, as well as prestigious, when your customers can have their crystal replaced and their watch returned in a short time frame.

www.watchfix.com
www.watchrepairvideos.com
www.watchrepairbooks.com
www.watchrepairseminars.com

219

Chapter 10
Outsourcing –
Finding the Watches Your
Customers Want

No matter what you have in your watch showcase, many customers are looking for the watch you don't have. How can you keep or make that customer yours? Outsourcing.

✓ Outsource Watches for Your Customers' Requests

It's not necessary to stock every kind of watch, or even to carry a large inventory of any watch. I'm sure what I have to say now won't score me any points with watch company reps, but I do not recommend carrying any specific watch brands.

✓ It's Not Necessary to Carry a "Line" of Watches

Let me clarify. Gone are the days when watch companies even contemplated courting retail jewelers with their loyalty. Everyone has either experienced or heard stories like this: A watch company sells you their line. A few months later you see it at a 50% discount at your local discount retailer. Invariably, the watch company rep says that he knows nothing about it. This may actually be true, but it doesn't take away the damage done.

In this section we are going to show you how to retail watches like the big guys, no matter what size your store is.

Brand loyalty of retail jewelry customers is as fleeting as the wind. No longer do people pick a watch solely on brand loyalty or the recommendations of the retail jeweler. People's buying choices are mitigated by everything from the latest James Bond flick to what Jay Leno was wearing last night.

You can use this to your advantage through outsourcing. There isn't any major watch manufacturer whose watches cannot be had through outsourcing.

The first thing we will deal with is how to cultivate the customers who are looking for a specific brand. In chapter 3 we discussed placing a small classified ad in the local Sunday newspaper. That ad simply states "Buying, selling, trading, repairing Rolex watches, Your Name and Address, [and] 'Not affiliated with Rolex USA'". This ad attracts these types of customers very effectively.

Also, a sign in your store stating that all brands of watches can be special ordered is very effective as well.

✓ *Cultivate Customers with Inexpensive Yet Effective Ads*

Now, some tips on how to be involved in this part of the business.

- It is very important to ensure that your customer knows what he wants and is sincere about wanting to purchase the watch, and not just wanting to look at it. Many times customers will bring in an ad they saw in a magazine

- When calling one of the sources listed at the end of this chapter, it is critically important to know whether or not you require the watch on memo, or is it a sold, invoiced order. Many outsourcers consider the watch sold and non-returnable when it has shipped.

- Avoid discounting too deeply. Many times the reason why someone is looking has nothing to do with price and everything to do with availability.

- Rather than offering a discount at all off retail, many times the sale becomes more attractive to the customer if you offer a two-year warranty, rather than the usual one-year.

Following is a list of outsourcers that we have dealt with and can recommend. Even if you never intend to resell a watch you buy from a customer to the public, many of the sources named here are very eager cash buyers. This revenue source should not be overlooked.

Most of the companies listed here are NOT authorized dealers in these brands, however, they trade in pre-owned as well as new inventory.

Inventory Adjusters, Inc.

3437 East McDowell Rd.

Phoenix, Arizona 85008

602-278-5966

FAX: 602-252-4598

Website: www.inventoryadjusters.com

Inventory Adjusters deals in everything from Timex to the occasional Rolex, and everything in between. They deal in closeout watches from major department stores and retailers. They also have great selections of fashion watches at very reasonable prices.

Serges & Co.

3841 W. Broward Blvd.

Plantation, FL 33312

1-877-973-7437

954-791-8446

FAX 954-583-6559

Website: www.serges.com

Serges & Co. Estate Jewelers specializes in fine quality pre-owned timepieces. They buy, sell, and trade all major brands.

www.watchfix.com
www.watchrepairvideos.com
www.watchrepairbooks.com
www.watchrepairseminars.com

225

Watch Material Suppliers

Cas-Ker Company

2550 Civic Center Dr, P.O. Box 31167

Cincinnati, OH 45231

Ph: 513-674-7700, 800-487-0408

Fax: 800-487-5848

email: casker@casker.com

website: www.casker.com

Book II

Keys to Successful Selling

www.watchfix.com
www.watchrepairvideos.com

www.watchrepairbooks.com
www.watchrepairseminars.com

There are two methods generally used for teaching. The first is to teach in a way that impresses the person being taught with all the esoteric information the teacher possesses. The second way is to impart to the student what the student needs to know in a way that he or she can absorb.

In this book we've opted for the latter method. In my years of teaching people sales and watch repairs, we have found that our students achieved their greatest successes by our imparting to them "what they need to know to be successful." This is what we strive to do with this book.

This book is oriented to be a book you can browse through. Ideally, you should take one concept per week and make it your own. The most successful salespersons I know have excellent habits. If you do not have excellent habits, let this book be an introduction to this concept.

Some of the things outlined in this book will absolutely require you to *"step outside of your comfort zone."* I strongly recommend you do. For most of us, our comfort zone consists of mediocrity, conformity, and stagnation. Make an effort. The most valuable person in any business environment is the person who can sell and close the deal. Make the decision that you are this person.

PART 1 – UNDERSTANDING THE CUSTOMER

WHY DOES A CUSTOMER BUY?

To be successful salespersons, we must first know the needs, wants and desires of our customers and how our products and services can help that customer with his needs, wants and desires. The real trick is spotting which emotion is driving the sale. We must isolate which one of these emotions is the customer's motivation. There is only one way we can know for sure which one will work, and that is by questioning the customer. The questions we ask will determine which one of the five emotions listed below is the dominant motivation.

The five emotions that drive a sale are:

Love   **Fear**

Need   **Pride**   **Profit**

Without any one or a combination of these five emotions, nothing can be sold. Let's examine the purchase of three items: a diamond ring, a fire alarm and life insurance, using the five emotions.

Love: there are many reasons why someone would buy something for love. Some of the more obvious ones would include buying a diamond ring for your wife or girlfriend. Some of the less obvious reasons would include buying a fire alarm for your house because you love your family, or buying extra life insurance so that the ones you love won't be burdened when you're gone.

Fear: one can buy a diamond ring for his wife or girlfriend if he feared losing them. One could buy a fire alarm because he feared dying in a fire. One could buy extra life insurance because he feared the disgrace his family would undergo if he died underinsured.

Need: a person could buy a diamond ring for his wife or girlfriend because he truly felt they needed it. One could buy a fire alarm because he truly felt he needed it, and one could buy extra life insurance on the rationale that he truly felt he needed it.

Pride: One could buy a diamond ring for his girlfriend or wife because he was proud of her. One could buy a fire alarm because he was proud of his home, and one could buy extra insurance because he was a proud person.

www.watchfix.com
www.watchrepairvideos.com
www.watchrepairbooks.com
www.watchrepairseminars.com

235

Profit: people sometimes buy diamonds in the hopes that they will profit from the purchase. People sometimes buy fire alarms for their homes because of the increased resale value of their homes by doing so (profit), and people may buy insurance for the cash value it accrues (profit)

As you can see, any of the five purchase-motivating emotions or any combination of them can be used in virtually any product. However, only one will be the dominant motivator for your customer.

Key to Successful Selling #1:

Determine what the customer's needs, wants and desires are. Then determine which emotion is driving the sale.

HOW DOES A CUSTOMER BUY?

There are only three basic types of sensual experiences as it relates to sales. They are:

Visual (seeing)

Audio (hearing),

and Kinetic (touching)

Each of your customers has only one form of sensory experience that is dominant. This is important to know because when we can relate to our customers within *their* frame of reference, it is a pathway directly to their mind.

Fifty-percent of the people in the world are visuals. Thirty-percent are audios and twenty-percent are tactile. It stands to reason that at least half of your customers are visually oriented. Therefore, until you know otherwise, it's a good idea to begin your presentations as though your customers are visually oriented.

When you have the occasion to meet someone who shares the same hobby with you, don't you automatically feel at ease? Let's say you're really into NASCAR racing, and you serendipitously meet someone in a supermarket checkout line who happens to be buying a magazine on NASCAR racing. It wouldn't be out of the ordinary for you to say something to strike up a conversation would it? This is because you have a matching frame of reference.

The same is true in selling. If we can match the customer's frame of reference in our sales presentations, more of what we say will be heard on both the conscious and unconscious levels. The more we can get the customer to hear what we are telling them, the more easily they will buy.

Visuals:

Persons with a visual frame of reference tend to speak in visual terms. They may respond with phrases like, "I'd love to see that," "Can you show me that," "Can I take this home to show my wife," "I see what you're talking about," "I'd buy it if I could only see a clear way to pay for it." A person who uses these types of expressions in response to your sales interview is a visually oriented person.

When conducting a sales interview with a visually oriented person, it makes no sense to talk your way through it. Use visual metaphors. If in the course of your sales interview you have the occasion to use a presentation folio, they are waiting for you to use it. If in the course of your sales presentation you have the occasion to actually show them the product, do so often and soon. In our sales presentation it's important to speak within the visual frame of reference. We could say phrases like, "Let me show you..." "Can you see how..." "Imagine how this will look..."

It's also important to consider the language we use in describing our product. Be sure to use visually descriptive terms and adjectives in describing the benefits of owning your product. For example, we could say "Imagine how this new car will look in your driveway," "If you could only see what I see, you would have to have this." Another way of identifying someone who uses a visual frame of reference is how he or she looks. Persons with this type of orientation tend to be very well dressed and tend to be particular about their hair [it won't be messy]. They also tend to like jewelry, and might wear quite a bit of it. Their cars are clean and polished; you won't find empty fast food bags cluttering up the backseat. Their yards will be neat and trimmed. This is because they see the world in visual terms more vividly than those who are not visuals.

www.watchfix.com
www.watchrepairvideos.com
www.watchrepairbooks.com
www.watchrepairseminars.com

242

Audios:

People with an audio frame of reference tend to speak in terms of how things sound to them. They may say things like, "I hear what you are saying," "That doesn't sound right to me," "It's just music to my ears." You'll notice that all these quotes are linked to sounds. Audios don't see the world as well as they hear it, so when selling to audios, our sales presentation needs to be geared around how it will sound to the customer. Use audio metaphors. We need to ask the customer often, "How does this sound to you?"

Also, it would make no sense to get out your sales presentation folio and start asking them to look at things with you! It would, however, make all the sense in the world having them *tell* you how they feel often. Audios love to tell you what they think. They also love to explain things to you, and they love to ask questions.

Many salespersons misinterpret the audio who has many questions as being a pain in the neck customer or someone who's trying to find a way to not buy the product. Nothing could be further from the truth! Actually, audios are just as easy to sell to as any other customer. We need only to understand their ground rules. They *hear* the world in far more vivid terms than others, and because of this we need to speak to them in terms to which they can relate. Use adjectives that center around sounds. For example, "This low payment will be music to your ears." "This car does 0 to 60 in 6.5 seconds. Can you imagine what that sounds like?" "Think of all the positive comments you are going to get from your family for buying this." You'll notice that these were tied and targeted directly towards the audio oriented person. This type of person also enjoys music -- I mean *really* enjoys music. He may be a "deadhead," he may be a sustaining charter member of the Philharmonic society, or maybe he belongs to Toastmasters.

www.watchfix.com
www.watchrepairvideos.com
www.watchrepairbooks.com
www.watchrepairseminars.com

244

Tactile (Kinetic):

Tactiles *feel* things more keenly than they see or hear. They tend to talk in terms of how things *feel* to them. For example, "This just doesn't feel right to me," "I would love to give it a spin." Use touchy-feely metaphors. They also love to have things in their hands, so if you have product to show them, give it to them, put it in their hands. If you have paperwork for them to look over and sign, hand it to them. The tactiles also like a pat on the back and are prone to give you a pat on the back. A good way to get a tactile's attention while you are talking to them is to touch them on the shoulder gently. This tends to open up their minds.

Key to Successful Selling #2

Every customer has only one form of sensory experience that is dominant. Match your customer's frame of reference when giving your sales presentation.

PART 2 -
YOU, THE SALESPERSON

www.watchfix.com   www.watchrepairbooks.com
www.watchrepairvideos.com   www.watchrepairseminars.com
247

THE SHOPKEEPER
Author Unknown

I believe if I owned a shop or store,
I'd drive the grouches from the floor.
I wouldn't let some gloomy guy
Offend those who come to buy.
Or have a salesman or clerk
With mental tooth-ache in his work.
Or let someone who draws a pay
Drive customers of mine away.

I'd take the the guy who takes my time
And only spends a nickel or a dime
And let him know I truly feel
That I was glad to have the deal
For one day who can tell
He may want the things I have to sell.
And then how glad he'll be
To invest his dollars all with me.

The reason why a customer passes one door
To patronize another store,
Is not because the busier place
Has better shoes, gloves or lace
          (- or lower prices -).
The biggest difference I believe,
Is in the treatment folks receive.

WHO YOU WORK FOR

We must always put the customers' interests first. *Our success as salespeople is completely dependent upon it.*

We've all heard it said that puppy dogs and young children know immediately and instinctively if you like them. Customers are no different. They instinctively know if we have their best interest at heart and if we truly believe in the products we sell.

It has been said many times (but it still bears repeating) that the fastest way to get rich with money is to place the customer's interest first. No one can long prosper without helping others to prosper in kind.

For those of you who need to view it this way: *Help your customers get what they want out of the time they spend with you and they will help you get what you want from the time spent with them.* The time you spend with your customers should be a truly enriching experience for both of you.

For those of you who are movie buffs, I'm sure you all remember the scene in "Godfather II" in which Michael Corleone and Hyman Roth were discussing business in

www.watchfix.com
www.watchrepairvideos.com
www.watchrepairbooks.com
www.watchrepairseminars.com

249

Havana. In this scene, Hyman Roth tells Michael, "I always made money because Hyman Roth always made money for his partners."

What we are trying to achieve in sales is basically the same thing. We want our customers to look forward to talking with us. This is easy to achieve if we place the customer's interest first.

This not only affords us the moral justification for us being in "the convincing" business, it is the fuel that drives the salesperson's motor. I like that term I just used, "the convincing" business, because there's no other term I know of that can better describe the sales business. We must always remember that our customers have literally millions of competing companies and ideas battling for their dollars.

Hands down, the companies and ideas that have the greatest success in getting customers to spend their dollars with them are those companies that best convey to consumers that these offerings have their best interest at heart.

For those of you who work in the service business, it is essential for you to remember what is at the core of what you sell: "service." By definition, service is giving the customer comfort in a timely manner. No matter what type of service we sell, we must be ever vigilant that our real purpose is to service the customer in a manner that is convenient and timely for them. Without this we have very little to sell, and no moral basis for selling it.

There are many ways of expressing this. In terms of familiar television commercials, Geico auto insurance says they have the best claim service and the lowest prices. That is one way of expressing, "We have your best interest at heart." McDonald's used to say, "You deserve a break today." Now they say, "We love to see you smile." These two concepts both embody the same message: "We care about you."

You'll notice in these McDonald's commercials they virtually never mention their food. Curious as it is, most restaurant commercials lack any mention of the quality of their food. The reason they do this is because they are appealing to the emotion that best suits the products they are selling. I'm sure you can think of dozens of slogans from ad campaigns and they all seem to have one central thing in common: "placing the customer's interests first."

If we truly have our customer's interests at heart, our foundation for sales is grounded in pure bedrock. Your features, your benefits, the longevity of your company, all are

www.watchfix.com
www.watchrepairvideos.com
www.watchrepairbooks.com
www.watchrepairseminars.com

251

distant seconds to placing your customer's interests first.

I've heard it said that when Dr. Jonas Salk was developing the polio vaccine, when he was closest to actually perfecting this vaccine that would save the lives of millions and prevent millions of children from going through life with crippling disabilities, he spent a good deal of his time selling donors and benefactors on helping him with the finances necessary to develop this vaccine. It truly can be said that Dr. Salk had the best interest of his customer - the world - at heart when he embarked on his sales pitch to cure polio.

I realize that comparing curing polio to what you sell may be a stretch, but you understand my point.

We need to be so certain of the products and services we sell to our customers that we need to feel guilty when they don't buy.

Let's say you are selling whole life insurance. The premiums are affordable to the customer and it offers peace of mind and cash value that in 25 years will be worth $100,000 to them. Given the fact that most people have woefully inadequate retirement plans, isn't it worth your time to help them see the benefit of owning it?

What if you sell training for business owners and you

www.watchfix.com
www.watchrepairvideos.com
www.watchrepairbooks.com
www.watchrepairseminars.com

252

have a training package that costs $1,000. The average net profit gain per year from the students of this course is $25,000. Don't you have a moral obligation to do everything in your power to help business owners see it?

That is why I say, "Believe in the products you sell." The products you sell really will help your customer, such as making them more money, making them more comfortable, making them more sexy, making them look better, etc. As long as it gets them what they want out of the time they spend, and it's fair, reasonable, and true, then you have every obligation in the world to help them see it. Failing to do so may actually make you morally delinquent!

I really mean this! I have a colleague who is in the information sales business. He complained to me that his close ratio was very low on an upcoming seminar he had planned. I asked him how much the seminar costs. He said, "$295." I asked him how much money his average attendee could expect to net as a result of their attendance. He said his average attendee made an additional $20,000 in the year immediately after attending one of his seminars! At this point, I said, "You should be ashamed of yourself." He was quick to ask me why. I told him that if he had a product that

www.watchfix.com
www.watchrepairvideos.com
www.watchrepairbooks.com
www.watchrepairseminars.com

253

would truly benefit the customer then he had no business giving up on closing with them.

I'm sure you're thinking what I was thinking when I had this phone call with him. He must not have explained what he was offering in a way that the customer could understand it. If he had, who in their right mind would say no to an offer that cost them $295 and netted them $20,000? What salesperson with a good and straight moral compass could allow his customer to say no when he had something that good to offer them? So I told him to go back to everyone who said no and apologize for not explaining his offer well enough. If he had, there would be no way they could have said no. I guess you know how the story ended: he filled the seminar!

Consider the fact that he had 30 people in his seminar with a net profit gain of $20,000 each. He enriched these attendees to the tune of $600,000 collectively. If that's not a good reason to get excited and to feel guilty for not helping our customers see the benefits of ownership of our products, then there isn't one that exists.

Key to Successful Selling #3

Always put your customer's interests first. Service your customers in a manner that is timely and convenient for them. Believe in the products you sell and help your customers to believe in those benefits.

www.watchfix.com
www.watchrepairvideos.com
www.watchrepairbooks.com
www.watchrepairseminars.com

255

ATTITUDE

The first thing our customers should notice is our confidence in the products and services we sell. The public is desperately seeking business professionals and salespersons they can truly believe in. If we are only half-sold on the products we represent then it must follow that our customers will only be half-sold -- and *half-sold customers do not buy*.

If you're not completely sold on the products and services you represent, then you need to get that way. There's one thing you'll never be able to conceal, and that is whether or not you are truly sold on your own product. We must be so sold on the products and services we represent that we are absolutely confident in them, because - either way - it shows.

Customers are only echoes of what we first present to them. By echoes, I mean that our customers can only get as excited as we are. We are in complete control of our customers' emotions by means of what type of attitude and emotions we present to them. The control of our customer's excitement, anticipation and eagerness to buy rests solely with us. Few salespeople realize what an awesome power this is. *The customer's responses to our sales initiatives will always be in direct proportion to the amount of excitement and passion we bring to the meeting.*

Key to Successful Selling #4

Be absolutely confident and believe in the products or services you sell. Show your excitement and passion – it's contagious.

GOALS AND OUTCOMES

Most sales trainers stress the importance of setting goals. Setting goals is an excellent idea, but I'd like you to think of them in a different manner:

Everything we do in the physical world creates an outcome.

A clear, precise goal is a great thing to have. You may have a goal of making $1,000,000 this year. (Having a goal of making "lots of money" is not clear or precise enough.) However, a goal alone is not enough. If you view your goal as the outcome of specific actions, that goal will then become achievable.

When we set a desired outcome, certain syntax must be used. It becomes automatic to list everything that must happen for this outcome to take place.

Let's take apart that you want to make $1 million this year. Let's say you are a salesperson who sells paper products on the road. In order for "I want to make $1 million this year" to become a reality, we need to know, step-by-step, all the processes necessary to achieve this.

Let's say you made $200,000 this year by visiting 200

customers and selling half of them. What would you need to do in order to increase $200,000 to one million? How many customers would you have to visit this year? How much better than 50 percent would our close ratio have to be? How much more effective would you have to be in gathering referrals?

Make a list of everything you'll need to do. Then -- and this is very important – ask yourself this question about each item on your list: *"Is it absolutely necessary that I (blank), in order to achieve my goal"?* If it's not absolutely necessary, ***DON'T DO IT!!!*** With this in place we will have an exact recipe of how to achieve the outcomes we desire.

By looking at the above listed scenario, isn't it obvious that in order to make $1 million, this salesperson would have to become five times more effective than he is currently? I'm not saying that in a sarcastic or skeptical manner. It's easy to become five times more effective as a salesperson when you know what it is you do that makes you as successful as you are.

Key to Successful Selling #5

Achieve your goals by making them the outcomes of specific actions.

WHO DO YOU SEE?

Years ago, many car dealerships would have a full-length mirror in the salesmen's break room. Stenciled at the top of this mirror would be the words, "Would you buy a car from this man?" The real intention of this mirror and the slogan above it wasn't to ensure that your tie was straight and your shoes were shined. The true intention was so you would see what you really look like. In the mirror, would you see a person who looked confident, who looked eager, and, most importantly, who looked happy?

We need to constantly be on guard that we do not telegraph our disappointments to our customers. We all have disappointments or bad days. Most are not sales related. We may have had an argument with our spouse, or have money problems, or maybe we just don't feel like selling. Be happy, bright, and exicted! Customers seek out sales persons that make them feel happy, exicted, and those who have a bright alert attitude. Be that person and they will seek you out.

www.watchfix.com
www.watchrepairvideos.com
www.watchrepairbooks.com
www.watchrepairseminars.com

262

Key to Successful Selling #6

Know what you really look like. Look confident, eager, and happy.

YOUR STYLE

In a world filled with mediocrity and conformity, we must strive to find ways in which we can stand out from the crowd!

In the seminars I hold, I always wear my signature piece of apparel -- a Hawaiian shirt with colors not found in nature on it. Insomuch that my main audience industry is jewelry, I wear a three ounce, 18 karat gold ring with a 3 carat diamond on one hand, and a 1 ounce gold ring with a 1 1/2 carat diamond on the other. Of course, I'm not suggesting that you must wear over-the-top jewelry or clothes to be successful. I am, however, suggesting that you wear something that sets you apart from the crowd of conformists. Jackie Gleason always wore a red carnation in his lapel. Groucho always wore a backwards beret and, of course, his signature cigar. Some ways of distinguishing yourself without being garish could be an interesting motif tie, e.g., if you work in the automotive industry you could wear a tie with cars or an automotive theme on it. Another way might be a handlebar mustache.

A few years back it seemed like everyone was

www.watchfix.com
www.watchrepairvideos.com
www.watchrepairbooks.com
www.watchrepairseminars.com

264

wearing a cornflower blue tie. If it were me and everyone was wearing a cornflower blue tie, I would be certain to wear something completely different. I'm sure you've all seen the beginning of the Monty Python TV shows when John Cleese says, "And now for something completely different." That should be your motto. Stand out, be noticed.

The permutations are endless and as individual as you are. In a world of mediocrity, conformity and all-around boring people, be someone they can easily remember.

Key to Successful Selling #7

Do something to stand out and be noticed. Wear an eccentric tie, signature jewelry, etc.

SMILE

In the sales seminars I hold there is one topic that I virtually "beat to death" and that is to remind salespersons that *customers love to buy from happy people.*

The best way I know of to keep the customer completely at ease is to smile frequently, broadly, and sincerely. Think of the many times you find yourself in any type of retail establishment. You almost always find yourself gravitating towards the salesperson with a broad smile and happy demeanor. There are very sound reasons for this working in your favor.

Can you imagine someone wanting to buy a car or big screen TV or new house being a grumpy, unhappy person? No, the truth is that when people are deciding to make those types of major purchases they tend to be happy, and naturally gravitate towards salespeople who are happy as well. It's simply the law of natural attraction. You know, birds of a feather flock together. Like I said earlier, our customers can only mirror what we give them, so we need to be especially careful that what we give them is what they need, right down to the attitude we present. It's a natural tendency for humans

www.watchfix.com
www.watchrepairvideos.com
www.watchrepairbooks.com
www.watchrepairseminars.com

267

to move towards pleasure, and away from pain. It's easy --
just *be a pleasurable person to be around, and customers
will move towards you.*

Key to Successful Selling #8

Remember that customers love to buy from happy people. Always be pleasant and smile often.

INCLUSIVE TALK

There is a very common mistake that salespeople make, and I call it the "*I Mistake.*" This is when the salesperson speaks exclusively in terms that relate to him. Some examples of this would be, "I can show you," or, "I think I can get that." When we talk to our clients, we need to use pronouns that include them in the conversation. Instead of "I can show you," try, "Why don't we look?" Instead of, "I think I can get that," try, "Let's see if we can get this."

The more we include our customers in the conversation, the more they will buy. It boils down to having a personal conversation with your client vs. a monologue by you. This is inclusive talk. The goal is to include our customer in the conversation.

> **Key to Successful Selling #9**
>
> Include your customer in the conversation. Make the conversation personal.

PHOTOGRAPHS OF YOU

It's very important for our customers to remember what we look like. People are bombarded with faces on TV, in person and in retail establishments, to the point where it is very difficult for the average person to place the name with the face of anyone. This is especially true if you do business remotely, that is to say, you do business by telemarketing or mail order. It is a proven fact that people are much more prone to do business with someone with whom they feel comfortable. It is also true that the more they see your face, the sooner they will become comfortable with you. Sociologists say that it takes an average of 30 exposures to someone's face before they can begin to feel comfortable about you, and feel that they are beginning to know you.

We all use business cards, stationery, invoices, packing lists, Web addresses, e-mail, etc. Onto every one of these we can put a "head shot." Try not to have too broad or too happy a smile -- a gentle smile with a look of confidence works very well. I can tell you that I have visited retail establishments that have either received my newsletters or an invoice, or they have been to my web pages, and the first thing I hear is either, "You're Dan Gendron!" or at least, "You're that guy who holds those seminars!" It pays to use your face. Don't be bashful. For those of you who know me or have taken the time to read the outside jacket of the book you're reading right now, you can see my head shot. And if I'm not embarrassed to use *my* picture, nothing you could say could convince me that you shouldn't too!

Key to Successful Selling #10

Add a picture of you on your business cards, stationary, website, etc.

BE ORGANIZED

One of the best ways I know of for most salespeople to increase their productivity exponentially is to become extremely organized. Regrettably, most salespeople lack proper organizational skills. We need to make our days habitual.

I recently had the opportunity to train a very talented software sales engineer. He was very skilled at understanding and enthusiastic about explaining his product. However, the one thing he was sorely lacking in was his organizational skills. In speaking to several of his clients, they all waxed poetic about his knowledge of the product and how helpful he was, but they were uniformly disappointed in his follow-up skills, e.g. making callbacks and remembering to do what he had promised.

It may never be known how many sales he lost, how many customers he disappointed to the point where they would either no longer do business with him or would be very reluctant to refer their friends to him. For many of us in the sales profession, our favorite thing to do is interface with the customer. For the most part, we tend to be self-indulgent creatures (don't take this is an insult -- I am, too) and being self-indulgent, we have that tendency to only do the things that we enjoy. No one really enjoys keeping copious, neat records and doing what seems to be non-productive follow-up work, but it's just that term -- *non-productive follow-up work* -- which is an oxymoron in and of itself.

In my office we have a database that we call the "the pester list." This is the database we use to keep contact with the leads that we were unable to close. We use this list in many different ways, but most often we use it to send out mailers to keep in contact with those on our pester list. It's amazing how many more people buy our products every time we do a mailing from this list. However, this list would not exist at all if it were not for the fact that every time we spoke to a potential client we got the following:

Name:

Address:

City:

State:

Zip:

Phone:

Fax:

E-mail:

Comment:

It's a very simple thing to do, especially when you are fielding incoming phone calls. It should go something like this: "Good afternoon, this is Acme Co. How can I help you?"

"I'm calling about the widget offer."
"Great! My name is Dan, and yours is…?"
"I'm Bob Smith."
"And your address, Bob?"

And so on. If we do this every time we initiate a phone conversation with a potential client we will at least ***"get the name."*** It is very important to get the name. I realize it does require some discipline to do this each and every time, but the rewards are fantastic.

Think of all times you've answered the phone and never got the customer's name. Now think what your sales would be if you had gotten the name and created your own pester list. An average sale is about one-in-10 to one-in-20 every time you use your pester list. If you are using a pester list with 1000 names on it, then wouldn't you sell 50 to 100 people every time you used it? These people on your pester list are what is known in marketing as "targeted leads." These

www.watchfix.com
www.watchrepairvideos.com
www.watchrepairbooks.com
www.watchrepairseminars.com

278

people obviously have an interest in the product you sell, otherwise you would never have heard from them. Targeted leads can cost anywhere from a dollar to $100 each and sometimes even more. Even if you never sell them anything, these names can be sold or bartered for money or tangibles.

Key to Successful Selling #11

Maintain a high level of organization. Get the names of your customers, create a "pester" list and use it.

KEEP YOUR PROMISES

There are times in the excitement of making a sale that salespeople seem to be willing to promise almost anything. There's nothing wrong with promising almost anything, however there is much wrong when we do not deliver. The fastest way I know to develop the customers trust and respect is to keep all promises you make.

Never tell a customer anything that you cannot be virtually 100 percent sure you can fulfill. In a world that is replete with mediocrity and situational ethics, it's relatively easy to standout and become someone your customers can trust and count on. There simply isn't that much competition in the integrity department.

How many times in your own life has a business or salesperson let you down and made promises they knew they were not going to keep? If you are like most people, quite a few. But this does beg another question ... how many times have you referred your friends to someone who's done this to you? Do you unquestionably return to them to buy products? Or do you shop around the first chance you get?

www.watchfix.com
www.watchrepairvideos.com
www.watchrepairbooks.com
www.watchrepairseminars.com

281

We all know the answers, don't we? Keep your promises and if you cannot keep them, refrain from making them!

www.watchfix.com
www.watchrepairvideos.com
www.watchrepairbooks.com
www.watchrepairseminars.com

282

Key to Successful Selling #12

Keep your promises.

WHAT DID YOU SAY WHEN THE CUSTOMER SAID "YES"???

Most salespersons are completely unaware of which close they use that is the most effective for them and the products they sell. If we keep a sales diary along those lines then we will discover interesting patterns. You will suddenly notice the same closing question appearing in your diary over and over again.

The real purpose of keeping a sales diary isn't so that we have something we can brag about. It's real purpose is for us to know what sales techniques worked best for us.

Let's say an advertising salesperson started keeping a diary and discovered the most effective close he used was, "Advertising doesn't cost, it pays," along with the closing question. Wouldn't that information be valuable? There's so much we can learn by keeping a sales diary. Some of the information we need to include in a sales diary is:

Who the customer was.

What they bought.

When they bought it.

What did you say just before they said "yes".

Were there any needs, wants or requirements they requested to have in the future.

Did they have any referrals.

If they did not buy, why not? (Don't presume this. *Ask* them why they did not buy.)

Key to Successful Selling #13

Keep a sales diary.

QUICK – WHO ARE YOU???

YOUR "UNIQUE SELLING PROPOSITION"

Everyone in sales needs a "unique selling proposition" (USP). This can also be known as an "elevator speech," because it should be short and to-the-point enough for you to tell it to someone between floors on an elevator. For example, my unique selling proposition is *"Hello, I am Dan Gendron and I help retail jewelers turn a pain-in-the-neck into a profit machine."* It does create quite a bit of interest. It's supposed to.

Remember this when creating your own unique selling proposition: Choose your words carefully, because you don't have many. There are many good sales thesauruses available. The one we use is <u>Words That Sell</u> by Richard Bayan. We must be able to express the USP in the shortest time span possible, without diminishing its impact

Unique selling propositions are most useful when addressing and alleviating a problem in the mind of the customer. As you saw with mine, I alleviate pains-in-the-neck. Here are some other good examples:

"FedEx, when it absolutely positively has to be there overnight."

'Roto-Rooter, that's the name, and away go troubles down the drain."

"Geico -- give us 15 minutes and you'll start saving money on car insurance."

"Hello, I am John Doe and I help families with credit problems drive dependable cars."

You'll notice that the average word count per USP listed above is between 15 and 20 words, and with that small amount of words, some very powerful suggestions can be delivered to your customer effectively. What you want to achieve is to paint a picture in the customer's mind. Look at the FedEx slogan, "When it absolutely positively has to be there overnight." What appears in the mind of the customer isn't the words. What the customer sees is their package arriving at its destination tomorrow with no problems.

Now here's the important part -- *you must use it!* In order for you to use it, it must be fluid and natural, and it must roll easily off your tongue. So, *practice, practice, practice* your USP. I realize that to some of you using a USP may seem very corny, but I assure you if it's well thought out and used consistently, potential customers will remember you and your USP.

Key to Successful Selling #14

Create a "unique selling proposition." Practice it and use it often.

www.watchfix.com
www.watchrepairvideos.com
www.watchrepairbooks.com
www.watchrepairseminars.com

290

YOUR "MINDSET" -- ADOPTING POSITIVE MODALITIES

IMAGINED FEAR

If I were to place a 10-inch-wide, 20-foot-long plank across the parking lot, would you walk across it? Invariably everyone answers yes. Then I ask the same question with one change: Let's place the plank between two buildings, 10 stories up. No one seems to want to do it! In a cold analytical way, there is no greater risk of falling from that plank in either circumstance, but one part of the stimuli, the "10 stories up," makes people shudder in fear. This is because we inject into this scenario a past memory of the danger of heights. In just hearing the scenario we immediately hearken back to what it felt like, what it looked like, what it sounded like, to be on a high ledge looking down.

It is certainly true that we are able to control our emotions this way, so why not use that knowledge to control them in a positive way? Before you begin your day, try to remember your best sales day. How did you see yourself that day? How did you sound when you spoke? Did you sound happy? Did the world around you sound happy? Were you listening to music you liked? What did the world look like? Was it bright? Were the colors festive?

Before you begin any sales interview, go back in your mind to that time. How did you sit? What was your breathing like? What was your posture like? You will find that by re-experiencing and adopting that modality, you'll become the salesperson you were when you were at your best.

RE-LIVE YOUR BEST DAY!

If we adopt the physical and mental modalities we possessed when we were at our best, then we will experience the same results. Every salesperson has had a day during which no one could say "no" to him. This wasn't because the stars were aligned in a particular fashion or that he was having good luck. The real reason was because he possessed the correct physical and mental modalities. We need only to copy those modalities. The brain has no way of knowing if the stimuli we present to it is generated from the outside world or from inside us (through our own choice), but our mind will generate responses relative to the input stimuli regardless of its origin. What this means is your brain

www.watchfix.com
www.watchrepairvideos.com
www.watchrepairbooks.com
www.watchrepairseminars.com

292

completely trusts what you present to it.   Present to your brain only those thoughts that enhance you as a person.

www.watchfix.com   www.watchrepairbooks.com
www.watchrepairvideos.com   www.watchrepairseminars.com
293

Key to Successful Selling #15

Adopt the physical and mental modalities you possessed when you were at your best and relive your best selling day -- everyday.

Part 3
The Art Of The Sale

RETAIL SALES
May I help You???

In retail sales, the most common mistake made by enthusiastic salespeople is to ask the customer as soon as they enter the retail establishment, "May I help you?" You should know immediately that this question is incorrect. First of all, we don't know what the answer will be. Whenever we ask a question, we should at least know the answer we want. It has virtually become a self-defense mechanism for retail customers to automatically say, "No, I'm just looking."

In my experiences in retail sales, when I would approach a retail customer without even asking if I could help them, and they say, "No, I'm just looking," I would say (to break the ice), "Hello, Mr. Looking. I'm Dan Gendron. It's nice to meet you." What I'm trying to say here is the same rules apply in retail sales as they do in all sales -- we must use the correct syntax. We must warm the customer up.

In this process we do not warm the customer up by talking about baseball, football or politics, unless that is what they want to talk about. I usually start off with something very neutral, for example, "Nice weather, isn't it?" At this point the customer can say yes or no, but I haven't heard, "No, I'm just looking." If I haven't heard that then the customer and I are in the process of warming up to each other.

Try not to be in a hurry. I realize that this is especially hard to do for those of you who work on "Ups." (For those of you not familiar with the term, Ups is a system by which salespeople take turns waiting on customers as they come in the door. This is a very common practice among car dealers, furniture stores and the like.)

So let's get back to trying not to be in a hurry. This is important. It's very difficult to impart to the customer that we really care, that we really have their best interest at heart, if the first thing we are interested in doing is saying, "can I help you?" I think we've all heard this far too much. We hear this in virtually every retail establishment we go in to. It's become an automatic part of the lexicon. This does not take away from the fact that it's also incredibly mercenary, and truly sounds that way. Think of all the times you've had someone say to you, "may I help you?" "Can I show you that?" It should by now be abundantly obvious to you how absolutely absurd these questions sound. Just because they are currently an automatic part of the retail lexicon doesn't mean they have to be or should be a part of ours.

Key to Successful Selling #16

Avoid asking, "May I help you?" or other similar questions. Warm the customer up first.

GET THE NAME

You can't sell anything to anyone until you know who makes the sales decisions. What I am talking about here is "getting the name." It can also be called "locating the decision maker." Many salespeople fail to get the name, and in sales training we call this "selling in the lobby." The reason why we call it selling in the lobby is because it can be compared to trying to close a deal with the company receptionist. It's easy to expend all energy and effort selling to all the wrong people. The real trick is to save your energy, effort and steam for selling to the person who can say yes or no. Unless we "get the name," oftentimes we find ourselves selling to the receptionist, the assistant manager, or even the janitor. Particularly in the case of telephone sales, it is vitally important to identify who you're speaking to and what their capacity is.

For example, during the course of a telephone sales interview we finally get someone to talk to (that is after we've gotten past the ignore buttons, voicemail boxes, etc.) A good, direct question to ask at this point would be, "Are you the person at your company responsible for making these decisions?" You'll find that the person on the other end of the phone is very quick to tell you if it's them, and if not who it is. Even if you're unable to speak with the correct person immediately, you've accomplished more than you realize.

Early on in my career I spent a great deal of time "selling in the lobby." The reason for this was that this extremely direct question is sometimes very difficult to ask. However, it is only difficult in our minds. Put yourself in the position of the person on the other end of the phone. Would you like to listen to a sales pitch that did not pertain to you? Many times the person on the other end of the line is just too polite to let us know that we are barking up the wrong tree.

The only way I know of to prevent this is to ask questions. So in professional selling we often say, "Did you get the name?" The truth is, once you have the name, you're more than halfway there.

www.watchfix.com
www.watchrepairvideos.com
www.watchrepairbooks.com
www.watchrepairseminars.com

301

Key to Successful Selling #17

Get the name. Determine if the person you are speaking with is in charge of making the buying decisions for the products you sell.

WHAT DID YOU CALL ME?

Now that you have gotten *the name*, it cannot be stressed enough that we need to use it. The easiest way to remember someone's name is to use it properly and often! However, avoid using familiar first names unless we've asked permission.

Let's say, for the sake of this discussion, a customer's name is Robert Jones. It's important that we ask Mr. Robert Jones if it is okay to call him Bob or Robert, or would he prefer Mr. Jones. Let the customer decide. You may actually find many of them prefer to be called Mr. Jones or Ms. Jones or Mrs. Jones. If it puts them at ease, then it has achieved the outcome we desire. This all boils down to the lost art of ***being polite and asking permission.***

Many salespersons believe that they are familiar enough with their client to use their first name and this will help the client to be at ease. This will not always be the case. If only one in 10 of your clients prefers you not to call him Bobby Boy or some other equally familiar name, and will not buy from you as a result of this (or hampers your ability to close the sale), then we've eliminated 10 percent of

www.watchfix.com
www.watchrepairvideos.com
www.watchrepairbooks.com
www.watchrepairseminars.com

303

our available client base. At the very least, it interferes with rapport. So be polite and ask permission to be familiar with your clients.

www.watchfix.com
www.watchrepairvideos.com
www.watchrepairbooks.com
www.watchrepairseminars.com

304

Key to Successful Selling #18

Use your customers' name. Be polite and ask before using first names.

www.watchfix.com
www.watchrepairvideos.com
www.watchrepairbooks.com
www.watchrepairseminars.com

305

LOOK 'EM IN THE EYE

Shakespeare said that the eyes are the "window to the soul". When speaking to your potential customer, always remember to look them straight in the eye. There is a strong, non-verbal communication that goes on here. If you are looking away while you speak to someone, often they will not be able to trust you and even if you have the most wonderful product to sell, it will be difficult for them to buy. People believe that if you are looking them in the eye, you are telling the truth. And smile!

Key to Successful Selling #19

Always be sincere when you look your customer in the eye. This will build their trust in you. And remember to SMILE!

FEATURES AND BENEFITS

As I said earlier, we must show our customers that we have their best interest in mind. There are many ways that we as salespersons can express this in a way that the customer can absorb. Sales trainers would call this using a "features and benefits" list. I strongly suggest you have one.

Feature: a feature is what a product actually does or has.

Benefit: The personal convenience or assistance for the customer derived from a feature.

Here are some examples:

FEATURE	BENEFIT
50,000 Mile Warranty	No Maintenance Worries for 50,000 miles
Programmable Thermostat	Don't Have to Wake Up to Lower the Heat
Casters on Furniture Legs	Move the Furniture wherever you want with ease

Until we tie those features and benefits to our customer's interests, needs and desires, they are nothing but empty words. When we place our customer's interests first and we have benefits tied to our products (such as a lower payment or a longer guarantee), we now have something that enhances the well-being of our customers. This helps them to get what they want out of the time they spend with us.

Salespersons need to be ever careful that we stay away from concerning ourselves with features, but we can and should stress benefits as much as possible. A feature is a cold technical thing that describes a product. Stressing benefits directs a customer's mind toward buying.

It's simple to make a features and benefits list. We need to list all the actual features of the products we sell. For example, if we are selling a car some of the features could be:

- The length of the warranty
- The selling price.
- The monthly payment.
- The size of the engine.
- It's seating capacity.

www.watchfix.com
www.watchrepairvideos.com
www.watchrepairbooks.com
www.watchrepairseminars.com

309

- A 16 speaker audio system.

- Leather seats.

- A sunroof.

You'll notice that these features are cold and impersonal. As I have said earlier, you need to tie these features to a customer benefit. Now here's the same list expressed as benefits:

"John and Mary, think of the peace of mind you're going to have with a 50,000 mile warranty."

"John and Mary, there is no other car in its class that can boast such a low price."

"John and Mary, can you see yourself behind the wheel of this V8? No more being afraid to merge onto the freeway!"

"John and Mary, your family certainly isn't going to have to cram into a small car with this car's 6 seating

www.watchfix.com
www.watchrepairvideos.com
www.watchrepairbooks.com
www.watchrepairseminars.com

310

capacity."

"This car's audio system is capable of surrounding you in rich sounds with its 16 speaker audio system."

"John and Mary, imagine how luxurious it will feel every morning when you sit yourself down on the soft leather seats."

"John and Mary, wouldn't you agree that you're never too old to enjoy a sunroof?"

If we make the statement, "This car has a 50,000 mile warranty," the part that will be dominant in the customer's mind is what they are paying for the car, not the piece of mind of having a 50,000 mile warranty. However, when you ask the question, "Not having to worry about maintenance for 50,000 miles is something important to you, isn't it?" and the customer agrees, they are no longer fixated on the price or conditions of the sale and may become focused upon the benefit (what they'll get out of it).

Picture in your mind a large apothecary balance scale.

In one of the bowls of the scale is your customer's reluctance to buy, and in the other is the benefits of ownership. Until we tip the scale to the side of benefits of ownership, the customer cannot say yes. Therefore, you need to create an irresistible offer.

List of features

Converted into Benefits

= an *IRRESISTIBLE OFFER!*

Key to Successful Selling #20

Create a features and benefits list. Stress the benefits of ownership to your customers. Make it an irresistible offer by using the "benefits of ownership."

COST VS. VALUE

We must always be mindful never to challenge a customer's reason for not buying. However, one of the most common reasons why a customer may be reluctant to buy is because of price. Having a customer challenge you on the cost of your product is not the end of the world. What we need to do is *get the customer to concentrate on the value, not the price*. I have two children, a boy and a girl, and I have learned a few things about how to buy them bicycles. There are basically two ways to buy a bicycle:

1. You can buy one every six to nine months at one of the "X-Mart" stores!

2. You can buy ONE really good one, and pay two or three times as much as one from the "X-Mart" stores!

It all boils down to the cost vs. the value of the products you're buying or selling. As with the bicycles I mentioned, the "X-Mart" store sells bicycles in the $70 to $100 range. If we look at that over the course of one year (its useful life) then the bike cost around 35 cents per day,or $100 per year not to mention the cost of the aggravation of having to buy another one, or trying to get it fixed.

Now, let's run the numbers on the "more expensive," brand name bicycle. Its useful life is around 10 years. If the bike cost $250, that's an annual cost of around $25 per year, plus the peace of mind that it will not be a problem in six months.

So, if I was selling better brand-name bicycles and I had competition from the "X-Mart" stores, the only question I would have for the customer would be, "John and Mary, wouldn't you agree that spending $100 on something that may or may not last one year isn't as good a value as spending $250 on something that will last ten times as long?" When the customer answers "yes," the price objection has been defeated and you will not have to deal with it again.

In using this type of comparison to overcome the price objection, first of all, your number illustrations must be easily absorbed by anyone. Saying something will last time ten times longer and cost a fraction of what the other product cost over the long haul is how it must be represented. Customers are always looking for viable reasons for saying yes.

www.watchfix.com
www.watchrepairvideos.com
www.watchrepairbooks.com
www.watchrepairseminars.com

315

Otherwise they wouldn't be speaking with us at all.

www.watchfix.com   www.watchrepairbooks.com
www.watchrepairvideos.com   www.watchrepairseminars.com

Key to Successful Selling #21

Get your customer to focus on the value of the product or service, and not the price. Never sell the price – sell the value.

A
B
C
Always Be Closing!

www.watchfix.com
www.watchrepairvideos.com

www.watchrepairbooks.com
www.watchrepairseminars.com

CORRECT CLOSING SYNTAX

Most salespersons talk when they should be listening, listen when they should be talking, and answer questions when they should be asking questions. The reason salespersons do this is because they do not understand the syntax of selling.

Syntax is the order and correct procedure of any endeavor. You couldn't expect to start a car if you put the gas in after you ran the battery down from trying to start it. The same is true in selling. Not only must we have the correct ingredients but we must know when to put them in. It's very important to utilize the correct order and closing of a sale. "A confused mind never buys." Our customers always buy a product in their mind first.

www.watchfix.com
www.watchrepairvideos.com
www.watchrepairbooks.com
www.watchrepairseminars.com

319

The syntax of selling is as follows:

Warm-up: this is when we have a conversation with a customer about anything not pertaining to the products we sell. Some salespeople talk sports, others the weather. They tend to focus on things they, the salespeople, have interest in.

This is not the correct way to warm-up customers. I've seen far too many circumstances where salespeople talk about baseball to someone who has no interest whatsoever. We need to be studying our customers. Spend more time talking about their interests and you'll keep their interest. When I say study them, I mean look at them. In what are they interested? Where do they work? Are there pictures or plaques on the wall? If we are observant we will find appropriate subjects to use for warming up the customer.

I know I shouldn't have to mention this at all, but for safety's sake I will: never discuss politics or religion or make inappropriate jokes. The quickest way to deter customers forever is to disrespect his religion, his politics, or his morals.

Qualifying: this is one area that most salespeople gloss over or totally ignore. We have a tendency to believe

www.watchfix.com
www.watchrepairvideos.com
www.watchrepairbooks.com
www.watchrepairseminars.com

320

that everyone is "qualified" to own our products. Some customers have conditions that disqualify them.

Later on we will discuss objections, but before we do that we need to discuss conditions. A condition is different than an objection. A condition is defined as "any circumstance that precludes the customer from owning our products." Some conditions are: the customer simply cannot afford our products or legitimately has no need for our products.

It is never possible to sell over a condition, so in the qualifying portion of your sales interview what you're trying to determine is whether or not the customer is "qualified" to own our products. As in most of the things salespersons do, we determine whether or not the customer is qualified by questioning them.

Convincing: in this part of the sales process we explain the benefits of ownership of our products. We achieve this by using the **"Socratic method."** For example, when we ask the customer if having a three-year unconditional warranty is important to them and they say yes, they are beginning to buy. We do this by creating questions tied to the

www.watchfix.com
www.watchrepairvideos.com
www.watchrepairbooks.com
www.watchrepairseminars.com

321

benefits of owership of our products and services. When we can express these benefits in the form of questions the customer can agree to we are beginning to close.

Some examples of convincing questions:

- 50,000 mile warrantee is what you are looking for, isn't it?
- A long term payment plan works best for you, doesn't it?

When using this type of convincing Socratic method questions we are only looking for a gentle nod or some positive reaction to these questions.

Trial closes: in this part of the sales process we tie our benefits to questions the customer can agree to. The main difference between trial closes and the convincing portion of the sales process is that in the case of trial closes the aim and purpose is to prepare the customer for the ultimate "yes." This will mean they have purchased our products. Some examples of trail closes are:

So do you think the payment plan we discussed will fit into your budget?

Do you think the economy model will meet your needs?

Once we have asked a few trial closing questions and gotten

positive answers we can proceed to the final close.

Final close: this is where we actually ask them to own our products. In this portion we are as direct as we can be. When the customer says yes we must immediately move on to the next process without fail or delay.

Some examples of final closes:

Settling the details: I call this the "you'll buy it back if you don't shut up" portion of the sales interview. Once the customer has agred to the final close, the only thing you need to be doing is settling all details necessary to complete the sale. Determine what color the customer wanted, when they wanted it, which financing they wanted, etc. If we do not immediately jump to settling the details, the customer can go squirrelly and not buy. The customer who gets squirrelly because you did not settle the details when you were supposed to is often the hardest customer you will ever close.

Key to Successful Selling #22

Use the correct syntax for a successful close:

- Warm-up
- Qualifying
- Convincing
- Trial Closes
- Final Close
- Settling the Details

www.watchfix.com
www.watchrepairvideos.com
www.watchrepairbooks.com
www.watchrepairseminars.com

324

THE BENEFITS OF A BENEFITS LIST

All good salespersons should make a list of all the benefits of ownership of the products they sell. With this and a little effort, we can develop the "selling the benefits" questions for use in our sales presentations. Grammar isn't the most important part of this process, so don't be afraid of using questions that end with, "Isn't that true?" "Don't you agree?" "Isn't it?" "Wouldn't you?" etc. There are a few advantageous tactics for using these types of "selling the benefit" questions.

1. We should have questions made up in advance and have practiced them so they become fluid, flowing and sincere.

2. We should smile a very agreeable smile when we ask the question.

3. We should ever so gently nod our head in the affirmative while we look at the customer and are awaiting their response. I actually have never met anyone who could

consciously shake their head no while I was gently shaking my head yes and smiling. It is nearly impossible for someone to say no while you're smiling and nodding. Remember, be sure you look your customer in the eye.

4. Should the customer disagree and not buy the "selling the benefit" question, then we absolutely need to ask them why they feel this way. Perhaps the customer says it's because he or she heard that such-and-such company has a better warranty. This is why it is absolutely essential for us to know our products and our competitors' products. If you get caught with that type of answer from your customer when you ask the "selling the benefit" question, you absolutely, positively *must* be prepared to answer it in a way that you can overcome the objection.

Let's say someone has a lower price, but you have a longer guarantee. You could ask a question like this: "Mr. Customer, isn't it true that the lower price from such-and-such company isn't worth as much as the piece of mind our longer guarantee offers?" Once the customer has agreed to that, we can move on, however, until they do, we have nothing else to gain by proceeding.

Key to Successful Selling #23

Use your benefits list to create "selling the benefits" questions.

WHAT IS A CLOSE?

In the most simple of terms, the definition of closing as it refers to sales is: "Any question we, the salespersons, ask, that answered by the customer in the affirmative, means they bought."

Most salespersons know what a close is. Everyone seems to talk about it, but few seem to do it. The most unnecessary and energy-wasting thing is a salesperson that is afraid to close. The best way to close a sale is to ask questions. The questioning method of closing is called *the Socratic method*, named after Socrates, the Greek philosopher who spent his entire life questioning Greek society. The reason why we use the Socratic method in professional selling is that it is the only way in which we, as salespersons, can direct and control the sales interview process. The person asking the questions is in complete control at all times. If we have a product that will truly benefit our client, then we need to be in complete control. This is not a "power trip" kind of thing. It is our responsibility as professional salespeople. Remember that we always place the customers' interests first.

Some examples of Socratic method phrases are: "Isn't that right?" "Don't you agree?" "It's a beautiful color, isn't it?" "Imagine what your wife will think when she sees this. She'll be surprised, won't she?" "It's just what you're looking for, isn't it?" We use this method because *any categorical statement we make to the customer will be challenged in the mind of the customer.* However, *any question we ask to which the customer can agree is immediately accepted in the mind of the customer. Customers buy in their minds first.*

Think back to when you were a child, or your experiences as a parent. It is rare that you could TELL a child to do anything without an argument. But if you ask a child to agree with a concept, they will almost always do so. It seems to be a natural human tendency to immediately challenge any categorical statement made by a perceived opponent.

In sales, we absolutely *must* avoid having the customer put up these mental roadblocks that invariably occur when we make broad, categorical statements. For example, we might inadvertently say, "Our readers are tremendously loyal to our advertisers." What we need to understand is what

www.watchfix.com
www.watchrepairvideos.com
www.watchrepairbooks.com
www.watchrepairseminars.com

329

is going on in the mind of our customer. I'll bet you're already thinking it yourself, "How do I know your readers are tremendously loyal?"

When we want to impart to our customers a benefit of ownership, it is essential that we get them to agree and state that it is true.

Now let's try that again. "Mr. Customer, isn't it important to advertise in a publication that has loyal readers?" The moment the customer agrees, you will never have to go over that benefit of ownership again. (That is an example of "Selling the Benefit.")

Every salesperson has encountered this type of circumstance. You know, you go to see a very agreeable customer, you're going through your entire sales presentation, and you're just about confident that when you pop the closing question they will say yes. But when you do, they "go all squirrelly" and tell you, "I've got to think about it," or, "I've got to talk to my wife," or "Give me some time to check out some other companies."

The reason why this happens is that we presumed that because the customer was amiable, smiling and *seeming* to agree with us, that they actually bought all the benefits we presented to them. This could not be the case because if it were, the customer would have bought. So when we present benefits of ownership of our products, is essential that we get the customer to *state* that they agree that they are true! And -- this is *very* important -- *never, never, never interrupt a customer when they are answering a question you've asked.* Always wait for their response.

QUESTIONS, QUESTIONS

You'll notice here that I said questions. I did not say monologue. The difference is quite profound.

Try this: "Mr. Customer, it's important to you to do business with the company that has the longest warrantee in the business, isn't it?" You'll notice the question I asked was easy to say yes to, wasn't it? And it should have been, shouldn't it? The real difference here is who is in control -- and *you* should be, shouldn't you? The truth is, the person asking questions is in complete control at all times -- and you always want to be in control, don't you?

www.watchfix.com
www.watchrepairvideos.com

www.watchrepairbooks.com
www.watchrepairseminars.com

Key to Successful Selling #24

Use the Socratic method of questioning to close a sale. Avoid making broad, categorical statements. Ask questions that the customer can agree to.

www.watchfix.com
www.watchrepairvideos.com
www.watchrepairbooks.com
www.watchrepairseminars.com

332

TRIAL CLOSES

A trial close is any minor question we ask wherein the customer gets to tell us their true feelings about our products or services.

There are two types of questions: open-ended questions (these are defined as any question you ask that allows the customer to answer freely), and close-ended questions (any question we ask that corrals the customer's responses within a narrow frame of answers).

Some examples of trial closes would be:

"Do you like the color?"
"Is it the right size for you?"
"Doe you like the way this looks on you?"
"Does the payment meet your budget?"
"Is this car large enough for your family?"

You'll notice that all of these questions are open-ended. We truly want to know what the customer thinks. If they really don't like the color, then it would make no sense to try to sell it to them, but it would make sense to help them get the color they want. We couldn't do that until we asked. However, if the customer says, "I love the color," then we can move on.

There are rules for trial closes. I believe there is much confusion about trial closes because the only rule that salespeople tend to remember is that using trial closes is a good idea. We should only begin using trial closes once we've given the customer sufficient benefits of ownership and they agree that the benefits are true. Remember, a benefit is described in terms of what it will do for the customer. If a feature is that our products and services are guaranteed for the life of the product or service, then the benefit is never having to worry about future problems with the product or service.

Even if you are getting positive responses to your trial closes, remember -- a trial close is not a final close. You still have to finish the job, which requires you to *ASK FOR THE SALE*. Just because you lob enough trial closes doesn't mean the customer is suddenly going to give in and agree to buy without you asking. You still need to close the sale. One of the men from whom I learned to sell once told me, "Even saying, 'Are you going to buy that, Stupid?' is better than not closing at all!" Of course, I'm not suggesting that you call your customer "Stupid," but you understand my point. You *must* ask for the sale.

Let's say for the sake of this discussion that all your trial closes are successful, the customer answers in the affirmative, they love the color, they want the size, it looks good on them, etc. Then we prepare the way for the final close, during which we ask the customer to own it. Once you have received a positive answer to a trial close, you can create a final close.

www.watchfix.com
www.watchrepairvideos.com
www.watchrepairbooks.com
www.watchrepairseminars.com

335

Key to Successful Selling #25

Use open-ended questions in your trial closes. Once you and the customer are in-line on the product, ask for the sale.

CLOSING TACTICS

Here are several different types of closing tactics.

Puppy-Dog Close: the "puppy dog" is named for a big litter of puppies. Everyone knows someone whose dog had 8 or 10 puppies. Invariably that person may ask you to look after one of the puppies, knowing full well that you and the kids will fall in love with it and the chances of them ever seeing that puppy again are slim to none. That is why in the sales training arena we call giving someone something for approval a "puppy dog."

Some examples of this would be a car salesperson who, after a client came by to look at an expensive car, called the client and asked him to look after the car while he was away on a long weekend.

The scenario almost always goes something like this: the client parks the car in his driveway. It's a beautiful Saturday morning and he's out cutting his lawn. His neighbor cannot help but take notice of the beautiful, shiny new car in his driveway. The neighbor does the polite thing and says, "What a beautiful car you have." At this point the client can either say, "I'm watching it for a car dealer," or, "Thanks for noticing!" More often than not the client will say, "Thanks for noticing." (This works best with tactile types.)

Other examples of the "puppy dog" are a software salesperson giving the client a copy of the software to use for 30 days to see if it meets their requirements.

Furniture salespersons may have a piece of furniture delivered to the client's home so they can see if the furniture matches what they already have.

Risk-Reversal Close: The other variation of the "puppy dog" is the risk-reversal. This tactic is one where all the risk of whether or not the client will be satisfied with the product rests with the salesperson. One example is a thirty-day money back guarantee.

Have you seen the computer professor whose commercial says he will sell you your first training CD for only $6.95 and will refund that if you're not 100 percent satisfied? That is a form of the "risk-reversal puppy dog close."

The truth is that very few people, once deciding to take you up on a "puppy dog" or "risk-reversal" situation, ever return the product. The reason for this is that they would not take you up on it if they weren't nearly 100 percent sold in the first place. What finishes the job is the fact that all the responsibility for whether or not the customer enjoys the product rests with you. It's difficult for a customer who has even a passive interest in your product to say no to a puppy dog or risk-reversal situation.

Sears and Roebuck, over the course of many years, has perfected the risk-reversal close. I remember that when I was a kid Sears would have signs up everywhere saying, "100 percent satisfaction guaranteed." Because of this Sears sold more appliances than any other retailer did during that period.

In the case of intellectual property, e.g. software, etc., there is very little risk to be assumed by the seller. When we look at it, the only risk we assume is the cost of production. In the case of software, books, videos, etc., it is extremely small. What comes with more tangible products, e.g., appliances, furniture, etc., are that the chances of the customer actually wanting to return something that large creates as much trouble for them as it would for you.

The add-on sale: the add-on sale is an offer we make to the customer after they've made an initial purchase.

Think about the pizza delivery businesses that invariably ask when you place an order, "Did you want breadsticks with that?" "Did you want 2-liter bottles of soda with that?"

While-you-wait oil change businesses will ask, "Did you want the deluxe service?"

Dry cleaners ask if you want same day service. These are all variations of the add-on sale.

Rumor has it that it was a soda jerk at a Walgreen's drugstore somewhere in the South who perfected the "alternate choice add-on sale." This soda jerk would ask the customers at the luncheon counter if they wanted one or two eggs in their malt. Up to this point no one had ever put eggs into a malt at all, but this persevering soda jerk asked everyone who bought a malt how many eggs they wanted. Suffice to say the drug store sold thousand of eggs per year from that simple add on close.

This represents the implied alternate choice: one or two. It wasn't one or two or none. As you probably have already guessed, most people chose one egg. This

meant the soda jerk sold thousands upon thousands of eggs in addition to regular malt sales.

Avoid rationalizing that an add-on sale is not appropriate in your business because you sell cars, boats, carpet, whatever. The truth is that the add-on sale is one of the biggest moneymakers in selling.

The real trick with using these tactics is how you use it and your consistency. Let's say hypothetically that a particular car salesperson sells three cars per week. On each car he or she has an average commission of $100 that can be directly attributed to add-on sales. That's $300 per week, or $15,000 per year on top of his or her commissions for the cars themselves. Not bad for taking the time to ask. That's why the pizza joints I mentioned above fire any clerk who fails to ask about breadsticks and soda.

Key to Successful Selling #26

Practice different closes until they become fluid and natural.

Key to Successful Selling #27

Ask questions to determine what the true objection is. Have the customer confirm, re-confirm, and re-confirm again that they have only one objection to closing the sale. Then close on that one objection.

OBJECTIONS

An objection is a way that your customer says, "You haven't sold me yet." Many salespeople confuse conditions with objections. A condition is any factor that precludes the customer from owning our products, e.g., I live in an apartment, so I can't buy a pool.

Here are some typical objections you will hear:

- The price is too high
- I need to talk with my wife
- We're not ready to buy yet
- We're still shopping around

If you can't get the customer to tell you what the true objection is, we certainly need to ask.

However, we need to ask in a way that smokes out the true objection. One of the best way I know of to do this is to use "The Is-It Method." The way we use the Is It Method is to ask questions of the customer that we know are not the true objection. For example, if we have a sneaking suspicion that price is the objection, but for whatever reason the customer is reluctant to tell us that this is the true reason, we cannot continue with our sales presentation until we smoke out this objection. We may ask "Is it the terms?" "Is it my company?" "Is it the color?" The more "Is Its" you can ask, the more likely you are to hear the genuine objection. It's impossible to begin closing until we know what that is. I realize that it may take some bravado to use this method, but your closing ratio will go up precipitously once you choose to do so. Make an effort to step out of your comfort zone with this one. You'll be pleased with your results.

Pinning-down the ultimate objection:

Let's say you've arrived at the point where the customer has latched upon one objection to your final close. This is a very good place to find yourself. Your next course of action is to have the customer confirm, re-confirm and re-confirm that this is their only objection to closing the sale.

Start off with something like, "John and Mary, let me understand…there is only one reason why you're not buying today?" Once they have said yes and have confirmed to you there is only one objection between you and closing the sale, re-confirm it again. "John and Mary, if it weren't for the fact that [state the objection] you would buy today?" Once the

customer has said that, yes, it is true that they only have one objection and it is [whatever their objection is], confir back to them yet again. "So, John and Mary, [state objection] is the only reason why we can not do busi today?" Again they will confirm it. And when they do phrase it again -- "If it weren't for the fact [state the objec we could do business today?" At this point you'll never another objection from the customer.

The customer would have never confirmed three t in a row that this was the ultimate objection they had, w not true. It would not benefit them in any way, nor help with whatever it was they were trying to achieve by tellii this.

The let's say for the sake of discussion the cust doesn't like the payment, it's too high for their budget. basically, the only thing we need to do to close the sale lower the price or extend the loan and lower the payn At this point the customer must say yes or admit that were lying the times you had them confirm that it was only objection. I've never had a customer admit to Truth is it's easer to close knowing there is only objection and not a indefinate number.

www.watchfix.com   www.watchrepairbooks.com
www.watchrepairvideos.com   www.watchrepairseminars.com
344

www.watchfix.com   www.watchrepairbooks.com
www.watchrepairvideos.com   www.watchrepairseminars.com
345

FINAL CLOSE

A final close is the question that, when answered in the affirmative, means that the customer has accepted your offer for him to purchase your product. A final close might be, "Lets get you into this new car today!?" In a case like that, once the customer has answered in the affirmative to the final close (and this next part is extremely important), *anything you say that deviates from settling the details to complete the sale jeopardizes your ability to do so.*

For example, let's say the customer says yes to your final close and instead of settling the details you "chicken out" (or -- worse yet -- don't listen) and continue to go over the features and benefits. Now you have gone past the sale, back, almost, to square one. Why expend all that time and effort just to let the sale slip between your fingers?

Eventually you may be able to re-close that customer, but these have now become the most difficult sales to complete, because we failed to close them at the right time. So the rule again: if you get a positive answer to a final close, begin settling details.

One very effective final close is the "**Alternate-Choice Close.**" The alternate choice close is a close-ended question that leads to completion of the sale. It goes like this: "Would you prefer to pay cash or would our payment plan be more convenient?" "Did you want to do it Monday or Tuesday?" "Would you prefer the red or the blue?" Whatever the customer chooses, he or she has bought.

The Doorknob close: In most cases, a sale is not considered concluded until the return privilege or guarantee time has expired. Some examples are a thirty-day money-back guarantee or some pre-determined amount of time during which the customer has the privilege of returning the product. (A product or service that is sold in the consumers home has, by law, a "three-day rescind" period.) These are actually types of risk reversal closes. The reason why risk reversal closes are so beneficial is because it takes away from the customer the objection that they "need think about it."

Many sales organizations use this type of close and accept the returns that seem to be inherent in using a risk reversal close. There are, however, other ways around this. The doorknob close is one of them.

www.watchfix.com
www.watchrepairvideos.com
www.watchrepairbooks.com
www.watchrepairseminars.com

348

The first time I saw someone use the doorknob close, I was going along on a trial demonstration because I was considering selling a certain vacuum cleaner in the home. The salesman went through the sales pitch virtually verbatim, and predictably the customers, John and Mary, said yes. At this point it was necessary for the salesperson to present the customer with the paperwork that informed them of their right to rescind within three days, The salesman, being dutiful as he was, went through that process explaining it all to them. While departing salutations were completed, just as the salesman was about to reach for the doorknob to leave, he suddenly stopped, turned around, and looked both John and Mary in the eye as he said, "John and Mary, as you know, you have three days to rescind your sale and that is your right. But I've been selling vacuums for quite some time now and to be honest with you, it's got to be one of the most awkward things I ever have to do to come back to someone's home and pick up the vacuum because someone decided to rescind the sale. John and Mary, you are happy with your purchase, aren't you?" At this point there was a brief moment of silence that seemed like an eternity. John looked at Mary, then Mary looked at the salesman and said, "This is one house you won't be coming back to. This vacuum is mine!"

Another way I have seen it done is with software sales. Virtually all business software involves a learning curve. The curve differs with each customer. For some it's a minor hill and for others its Mount Everest. As you can imagine, many of the Mount Everest-type people return the product. One way of combating this is to explain what is necessary for them to be successful. For example, telling them that a certain software product has a built-in tutorial and that if they take the time to do one lesson per day, within a month they should be proficient. At this point, however, it is absolutely imperative that you ask a closing question -- "Mr. Businessman, you do have time to do one lesson per day, don't you?" When they say yes, we can say, "Virtually everyone is able to learn in thirty-days by doing one lesson per day. You feel comfortable that you're able to do that, don't you?"

There are many things working in your favor by using this type of close. No one wants to admit to being lazy, do they? No one wants to admit they're too stupid to learn, do they? By the way, I'm closing you right now, aren't I? And I

OBJECTIONS

An objection is a way that your customer says, "You haven't sold me yet." Many salespeople confuse conditions with objections. A condition is any factor that precludes the customer from owning our products, e.g., I live in an apartment, so I can't buy a pool.

Here are some typical objections you will hear:

- The price is too high
- I need to talk with my wife
- We're not ready to buy yet
- We're still shopping around

If you can't get the customer to tell you what the true objection is, we certainly need to ask.

However, we need to ask in a way that smokes out the true objection. One of the best way I know of to do this is to use "The Is-It Method." The way we use the Is It Method is to ask questions of the customer that we know are not the true objection. For example, if we have a sneaking suspicion that price is the objection, but for whatever reason the customer is reluctant to tell us that this is the true reason, we cannot continue with our sales presentation until we smoke out this objection. We may ask "Is it the terms?" "Is it my company?" "Is it the color?" The more "Is Its" you can ask, the more likely you are to hear the genuine objection. It's impossible to begin closing until we know what that is. I realize that it may take some bravado to use this method, but your closing ratio will go up precipitously once you choose to do so. Make an effort to step out of your comfort zone with this one. You'll be pleased with your results.

Pinning-down the ultimate objection:

Let's say you've arrived at the point where the customer has latched upon one objection to your final close. This is a very good place to find yourself. Your next course of action is to have the customer confirm, re-confirm and re-confirm that this is their only objection to closing the sale.

Start off with something like, "John and Mary, let me understand...there is only one reason why you're not buying today?" Once they have said yes and have confirmed to you there is only one objection between you and closing the sale, re-confirm it again. "John and Mary, if it weren't for the fact that [state the objection] you would buy today?" Once the customer has said that, yes, it is true that they only have the one objection and it is [whatever their objection is], confirm it back to them yet again. "So, John and Mary, [state the objection] is the only reason why we can not do business today?" Again they will confirm it. And when they do, re-phrase it again -- "If it weren't for the fact [state the objection] we could do business today?" At this point you'll never hear another objection from the customer.

The customer would have never confirmed three times in a row that this was the ultimate objection they had, were it not true. It would not benefit them in any way, nor help them with whatever it was they were trying to achieve by telling us this.

The let's say for the sake of discussion the customer doesn't like the payment, it's too high for their budget. Then, basically, the only thing we need to do to close the sale is to lower the price or extend the loan and lower the payments. At this point the customer must say yes or admit that they were lying the times you had them confirm that it was their only objection. I've never had a customer admit to lying. Truth is it's easer to close knowing there is only _**one**_ objection and not a indefinate number.

Key to Successful Selling #27

Ask questions to determine what the true objection is. Have the customer confirm, re-confirm, and re-confirm again that they have only one objection to closing the sale. Then close on that one objection.

FINAL CLOSE

A final close is the question that, when answered in the affirmative, means that the customer has accepted your offer for him to purchase your product. A final close might be, "Lets get you into this new car today!?" In a case like that, once the customer has answered in the affirmative to the final close (and this next part is extremely important), *anything you say that deviates from settling the details to complete the sale jeopardizes your ability to do so*.

For example, let's say the customer says yes to your final close and instead of settling the details you "chicken out" (or -- worse yet -- don't listen) and continue to go over the features and benefits. Now you have gone past the sale, back, almost, to square one. Why expend all that time and effort just to let the sale slip between your fingers?

Eventually you may be able to re-close that customer, but these have now become the most difficult sales to complete, because we failed to close them at the right time. So the rule again: if you get a positive answer to a final close, begin settling details.

One very effective final close is the "**Alternate-Choice Close.**" The alternate choice close is a close-ended question that leads to completion of the sale. It goes like this: "Would you prefer to pay cash or would our payment plan be more convenient?" "Did you want to do it Monday or Tuesday?" "Would you prefer the red or the blue?" Whatever the customer chooses, he or she has bought.

The Doorknob close: In most cases, a sale is not considered concluded until the return privilege or guarantee time has expired. Some examples are a thirty-day money-back guarantee or some pre-determined amount of time during which the customer has the privilege of returning the product. (A product or service that is sold in the consumers home has, by law, a "three-day rescind" period.) These are actually types of risk reversal closes. The reason why risk reversal closes are so beneficial is because it takes away from the customer the objection that they "need think about it."

Many sales organizations use this type of close and accept the returns that seem to be inherent in using a risk reversal close. There are, however, other ways around this. The doorknob close is one of them.

The first time I saw someone use the doorknob close, I was going along on a trial demonstration because I was considering selling a certain vacuum cleaner in the home. The salesman went through the sales pitch virtually verbatim, and predictably the customers, John and Mary, said yes. At this point it was necessary for the salesperson to present the customer with the paperwork that informed them of their right to rescind within three days, The salesman, being dutiful as he was, went through that process explaining it all to them. While departing salutations were completed, just as the salesman was about to reach for the doorknob to leave, he suddenly stopped, turned around, and looked both John and Mary in the eye as he said, "John and Mary, as you know, you have three days to rescind your sale and that is your right. But I've been selling vacuums for quite some time now and to be honest with you, it's got to be one of the most awkward things I ever have to do to come back to someone's home and pick up the vacuum because someone decided to rescind the sale. John and Mary, you are happy with your purchase, aren't you?" At this point there was a brief moment of silence that seemed like an eternity. John looked at Mary, then Mary looked at the salesman and said, "This is one house you won't be coming back to. This vacuum is mine!"

Another way I have seen it done is with software sales. Virtually all business software involves a learning curve. The curve differs with each customer. For some it's a minor hill and for others its Mount Everest. As you can imagine, many of the Mount Everest-type people return the product. One way of combating this is to explain what is necessary for them to be successful. For example, telling them that a certain software product has a built-in tutorial and that if they take the time to do one lesson per day, within a month they should be proficient. At this point, however, it is absolutely imperative that you ask a closing question -- "Mr. Businessman, you do have time to do one lesson per day, don't you?" When they say yes, we can say, "Virtually everyone is able to learn in thirty-days by doing one lesson per day. You feel comfortable that you're able to do that, don't you?"

There are many things working in your favor by using this type of close. No one wants to admit to being lazy, do they? No one wants to admit they're too stupid to learn, do they? By the way, I'm closing you right now, aren't I? And I should, shouldn't I? (This type of close works best with auditory persons.)

The Assumptive or "Order Blank" Close: The assumptive close is one of my least favorite closes. The reason is that its method is pure stealth. The way an assumptive close works is, once we've gotten past the convincing part of our sales presentation, rather than ask for the sale we just presume the customer has bought and begin settling details.

The reason why I'm at odds with this type of closing technique is that it assumes the customer is completely sold. *We can never know if the customer is completely sold without asking questions, can we?* The real danger in using the assumptive close is, if the customer is not actually completely sold it may be very difficult to get them that way once you have gone past that point.

Think of how you would feel if it was you and a car salesman or furniture salesman or a computer salesman who, after giving you all the benefits of ownership, starting asking questions like your name, your address, city, state, zip, phone, delivery time, MasterCard/Visa/American Express, etc., without giving you the opportunity to say you want to buy it!

The only companies that can use the assumptive or order blank close with any degree of finesse are service companies, such as car service, plumbers, etc. But in reality, that is not a sales environment, it is more of an order-taking, necessity environment. Perhaps this type of close used to work back when Ike was President and Edsels were cool, but today buyers are far too sophisticated to stand still for a somewhat deceptive "assumptive close." We simply have to be better than that. We have to truly sell them!

The Take-Away close: The take away close relies upon a contrived scarcity of product. For example, "There is a waiting list for this car," or, "Not everyone will qualify," etc. The problem with using this type of close is, once you have used it and failed, it becomes nearly impossible to ever approach that customer again on a sincere basis.

If I told you there was a waiting list for memberships to a certain health club and that you had to act now or risk not getting in, and then you tell me you need think about it, can I call you next month and tell you that we still have an opening? The answer is obvious. No, you cannot.

www.watchfix.com
www.watchrepairvideos.com
www.watchrepairbooks.com
www.watchrepairseminars.com

352

It is always better to be above-board with the customer. Never contrive circumstances to close. Tomorrow is coming, and if we do this to enough customers, we will soon run out of them.

The Summary or "Ben Franklin" Close: The Ben Franklin close is obviously named for Ben Franklin because old Ben once wrote in *Poor Richard's Almanac* about a way to equitably sort out a problem. Ben said to take a piece of paper and draw a vertical line down the center of it. On one side, at the top of the paper, write "pro" and on the other side write "con."

Ben then said to list all the reasons why you should do something in the "pro" column, and all the reasons not to in the "con" column. The summation of the pros and cons will speak for itself. This was good advice then and now.

The way we use this in our interaction with the customer is, we tell them the Ben Franklin story, then we take a sheet of paper and write all the reasons for them buying our products in the "pro" column, and their reasons for not buying in the "con." I will bet you that you can come up with more reasons why they should buy than they can come up

www.watchfix.com
www.watchrepairvideos.com
www.watchrepairbooks.com
www.watchrepairseminars.com

353

with reasons why they should not! This type of close works best with visually oriented persons.

Key to Successful Selling #28

Once your final close is accepted, settle the details!

REFERRALS

If we are not asking everyone who buys something from us for referrals then we are missing out on an enormous reservoir of potential customers. There is no better time to ask for a referral than when the customer agrees to buy our products. We needn't be afraid to ask. Once the customer has said yes to buying our products then there is no better time for us to ask them to tell their friends and relatives about our products and services. The majority of people you ask for a referral are only too happy to give names.

Some salespersons simply ask for the referral as soon as they finish the details and have concluded all business with the customer. There is nothing wrong with doing it this way, but let me give you a few other ways that work even better. Many car dealers offer free mats, window tinting, or even cash for the successful referral.

There are many different ways to cultivate referrals. Some are:

An incentive to your current customer base, such as gift certificates, discounts, or free samples. For example, if you are in retail jewelry, you could offer incentives to your current customer base by giving them $100 gift certificates for them to give away. These $100 gift certificates are redeemable on any purchase of $500 or more. Given the markup on jewelry items (which is most commonly 100 percent), giving $100 is not a big expense when compared to the average lifetime value of a steady customer.

You might have incentives to affiliate businesses, i.e., businesses that attract the same type of customer base but offer different services than yourself. For example, if you have a health food store, wouldn't it make sense to have an affiliate referral agreement with a health club, racquetball club, or even country club? This type of arrangement works best when it is reciprocal. If you both put out a newsletter, you both recommend each other in your newsletters.

Get involved with charitable organizations, i.e., churches, temples, and synagogues. These organizations are always looking for ways to expand their budgets. Getting a charitable organization to send you referrals on an affiliate basis is simple. Pay the organization a fixed commission on all referrals from them. It's also very good advertising to be affiliated with a church, synagogue, temple, charitable organization, etc., because any good-will their name gathers

www.watchfix.com
www.watchrepairvideos.com
www.watchrepairbooks.com
www.watchrepairseminars.com

357

can be harvested by you as well.

Key to Successful Selling #29
Ask for referrals from your customers.
Add an incentive for successful referrals.

Epilogue –Keys to Successful Selling

If you're like most people who read business books, you'll thumb through this as quickly as possible. I understand the rational for doing it that way. I myself read business books in much the same style. But I'd like to offer a suggestion. Go back and read this book again, item by item, slowly, and then take the ideas and make them your own.

There's a special kind of magic that happens when you make something your own. It becomes unique and a part of you. Good habits are formed from what we can learn from others, and what we can add to it.

There is nothing that is needed more in business today than good salespeople. They are, by far, the most essential part of any business endeavor. Some of the most gratifying parts of my business life have been accomplishing sales in critical situations. Learn to close with confidence and this ability will serve you and your customers and the companies you own and work for throughout your life.

Dan Gendron C.M.H.

Book III
Start Your Own PictureWatch Business

www.watchfix.com

www.watchrepairvideos.com

www.watchrepairbooks.com

www.watchrepairseminars.com

What is a PictureWatch?

A PictureWatch is a quality quartz watch with a family photo, company logo, Fraternal organization (Elks, Moose, Eagles, Masons, etc.), graduating class, birthday, anniversary, Christmas or Chanukah wishes, or just about anything you or your customer can imagine on the dial. Now you, too, can make PictureWatches with this step-by-step book.

We'll tell you what you'll need for computer equipment, software, printers and labels, where to get watches and how to put it all together. There is a tremendous demand for this highly profitable personalized service. With this easy-to-use, step-by-stem instructions, in virtually no time at all you, too, can have your very own, highly profitable PictureWatch business.

Many times I have heard the comparison to the $5 watches sold in airline magazines with company logos. Nothing could be further from the truth. First of all, those types of offers are for literally thousands of watches ordered at the same time, all with the same graphic on them. The lead-time is several weeks and the quality of the watch is not comparable to what you will be offering. Last but not least, those offers are not a "personalized service." What you will be offering is a quality quartz watch, not mass-produced by the hundreds of thousands, but one at a time, individualized to your customer's needs and tastes. As with anything that is personalized and of high quality, it costs more than a cheap substitute.

While we are on the subject of cost, we suggest a retail of $69 to $89, depending on your market area. For quantity discounts, we suggest you offer them from $35 to $55 depending on the quantity. Some examples of this may be company logos, employee recognition programs, school teams, and graduation watches, to name a few. These are highly profitable because once you have the design made, you simply duplicate it.

What do you need?

Computer Equipment/Supplies
- A computer with the capability to support color graphics and imaging or desktop publishing software
- Scanner
- Digital camera (optional)
- a color laser or color inkjet printer
- glossy photo quality labels (such as Avery 8763 www.avery.com)
- Most any desktop publishing software such as MicroSoft Publisher™, or imaging software such as Microsoft Image Composer™ or Adobe Photoshop™.

Watches
You will need a supply of quartz watches without calendars, with flat dials or with removable markers.

You can find suppliers in the Closeout News (323-525-2527 www.close-out-news.com). This publication is the trade publication of the closeout, surplus industry. Every month there are literally dozens of companies listed there that sell surplus quality watches, ranging in price from $3 to $20, depending on the quality and the name brand. Inventory Adjusters (602-278-5966 www.inventoryadjusters.com) is one of the companies listed in the Closeout News who we have found to be particularly helpful. Additionally, you might contact Closeout Jewelry Warehouse (727-345-6072 www.closeoutjewelry.com) for supplies of watches.

Ideally, the watch dial diameter should be 20 to 30 millimeters. If you use a watch smaller than 20 millimeters, the picture (particularly if it is a face) will be so small as to be unrecognizable. Some company or organization logos can be successfully applied on smaller watches. As a rule of thumb, if the picture or logo can not be recognized at arm's length, it is not suitable.

A good supply of watches can be had from surplus/close-out dealers. Most close-out/surplus dealers sell a quality watch – believe it or not – in the $5 to $15 range. The criteria we use for a "good" watch is a stainless steel back, mineral glass (sapphire) crystal, quality leather or metal expansion (Speidel™ -type) band and a movement that can be easily replaced if necessary.

Tools
- Loupe
- Case Knife
- Case spanner
- Screwdrivers
- Tweezers
- Hand removers (Bow or Scissors)
- Punch
- Case closer
- Dial Vernier
- Bulb Aspirator or Canned Air
- Rodico (dial cleaner)
- Silicon
- Ligne Gauge
- Cyclotron™

All of these tools can be obtained from Cas-Ker Co. (800-487-0408 www.casker.com)

How to use the tools:

Loupe –

Eye magnification style choice tends to be a very personal thing. However, **regardless of the type of magnification you choose, it is absolutely necessary to use it**. Without a loupe, "you will not be able to see that which you cannot see." And my father would add, "and what you cannot see is exactly what will get you into trouble."

There are three types of loupes:

www.watchfix.com   www.watchrepairbooks.com
www.watchrepairvideos.com   www.watchrepairseminars.com
367

Visor (Dual power, we recommend three and seven)

Monocle (3 power)

Spectacles (dual power, 3 and seven)

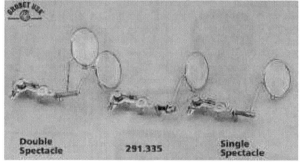

Case   Knife

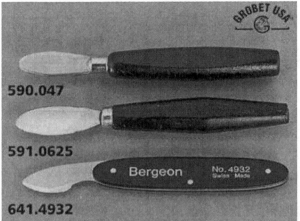

The type of case knife you choose to use is not as important as how you use it. A watchcase is not opened with force, like a clamshell. Just as Archemedes said, "Give me a place to stand and I will move the earth." I say, find the right place on the watch caseback (by using your

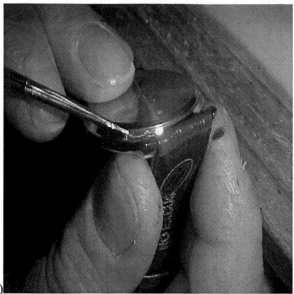

loupe) and
you can open any "snapback" watchcase with very little
force. Take a plastic bag or clear plastic tape and place it
over the case back so that if you slip, you will not damage
the case. Many make the mistake of pushing their way in as
hard as they can to open the case. This is almost sure to
damage the movement beyond repair. Simply get the knife
snugly against the caseback and bezel of the

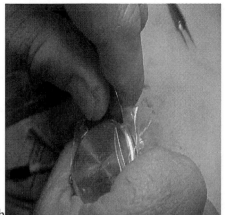

watch and gently twist
the knife until the caseback pops away from the bezel.

Case   spanner   -

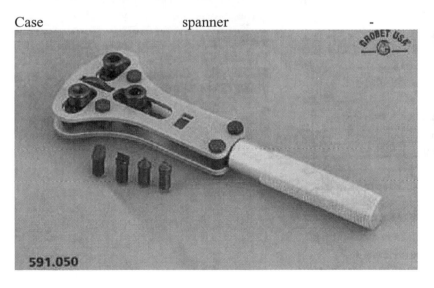

591.050

These are used to open casebacks that screw onto the bezel.
As above, use a piece of plastic baggy or clear plastic tape to

protect the case. A spanner has two adjustments to fit the three pins to the slots on the back of a screw-off caseback.

Fit the two top pins using the width adjustment with the thumbwheel and then fit the third by turning the handle, just snug enough to stay in place as you turn the caseback. (If you tighten them too much, they can pop out when you turn the tool.)

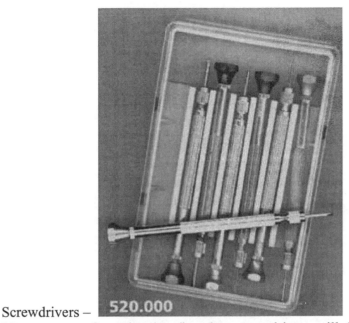

Screwdrivers –
Most any set of watchmakers/jewelers screwdrivers will do.
My personal favorite, though, is Bergeon or Bestfit. This is
because they have replaceable blades, and we all know how
often one can damage a screwdriver blade.

Tweezers —

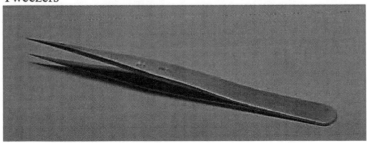

For most purposes, AA tweezers will suffice.

Hand Removers –There are two types of hand removers.

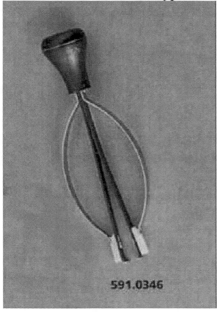

591.0346

Bow
These are the easiest to use.

Scissor

These are rather ancient, but still useable in a pinch.

Punch

I use a convocal jewel setting punch. This type of punch can be found in any staking set.

Case Closer –
There are many different types. If you already have one, regardless of what type it is, it should suffice. If not, a good sturdy one can be had for around $50.

Dial Vernier/caliper –In the jewelry and watch trades, we use millimeters (one-one thousandth of a meter.) The reason why we use millimeters as opposed to inches is because it is far more precise. We use the vernier/caliper to measure the diameter of the watch dial. A Leveridge™ gauge is also a millimeter gauge. There are two types,

digital   readout

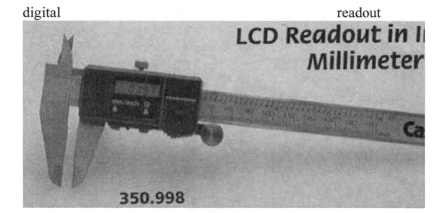

350.998

or   dial   vernier.

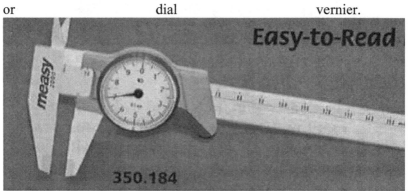

350.184

Either one will do.

Cyclonic™

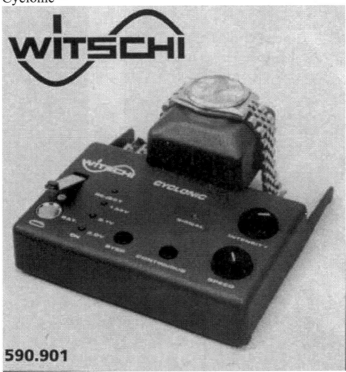

590.901

This is an electronic device that is used to determine that the hands have proper clearance after we have assembled the watch with the picture dial. Also, some quartz testers and timing machines have a stepping motor feature as well (when you press a button, it makes the hands spin around the dial, so that one can determine if the hands are touching.)

Making the Picture Dial

Selecting a Picture – Almost anything can be put on a dial, however, some guidelines will help you achieve better results and ensure better customer satisfaction. Remember, you are usually trying to fit a square peg into a round hole! Here is an ideal photo:

Photos:

- If there is one subject in the shot,

remember that you don't want the watch hands coming out of a person's nose, eye, belly-button or other "private part"! So you may have to make the subject a bit smaller and over to one side.

 You will then need to crop some of the background and add it where there is white space on the dial.

- If there is more than one person in the photo,  you may have to move some of the people by cutting out and pasting with your imaging program, to form them into a grouping that fits onto the dial.

- Pictures with a lot of background work well and are easiest to fit onto the dial area.

- Some pictures just won't be appropriate for smaller watch dials (like ladies' watch sizes), like a wedding party of 12, head to toe shot!

Logos
- Company, team or organization logos can be placed anywhere on the dial.

www.watchfix.com
www.watchrepairvideos.com

www.watchrepairbooks.com
www.watchrepairseminars.com

Preparing the dial – (NOTE: For the purposes of this CD, we will explain the process using Microsoft Image Composer and Microsoft Publish. Many other programs use similar steps...use the one you are comfortable with.)

- Open Microsoft Image Composer.
- Place the photo in the scanner.
- Click on File > New> File> Scan Image> Acquire Scan. Scan the photo or logo.
- Click on View> Fit Composition Space to Selection.
- Click on File> Save As. Then click file type .JPG, name the file and click Save.
- Close Image Composer.

- Using your vernier, measure the diameter of the dial in millimeters (a more accurate measurement than inches).

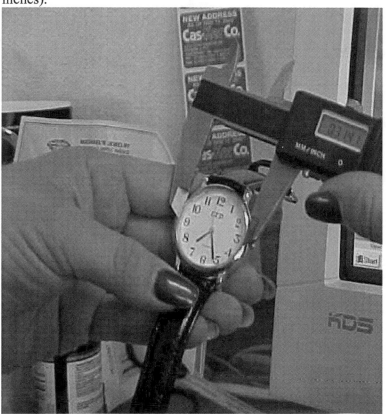

- Open Microsoft Publisher.
- Open a new, blank page.
- Click on Tools> Options. You will see a drop down menu for Measurement Units. Change that to Centimeters. A millimeter is $1/10^{th}$ of a centimeter, therefore, if your dial is 30 millimeters, your circle will be 3.0 centimeters.

- Click on the circle tool and create a hairline circle equal to the diameter of the dial.
- Create a picture frame over the circle.
- Click on Insert>Picture> From File and insert your picture file into that frame.
- Click on Arrange> Send to Back so that the circle is visible.
- Adjust the picture for the best size and placement of the subject within the circle.
- If you have white spaces around the picture but within the dial, make a second copy of the picture you are using. Then use your crop tool to leave just a bit of the background on that second image. Arrange the additional background around the image within the dial circle.

Pictures can be placed on any number of backgrounds, according to the time of year or occasion, such as a heart for Valentine's Day, Christmas tree, etc.

Additionally, you can add messages over or alongside the pictures.
- Create a text box over the picture.
- Click on the "Fill" icon and click "Clear" or "No Fill"

- Type in your message, colorize the text, and use an appropriate font.

Finally, locate the 3:00 position of the circle and place a small dot on the edge of it.

- Click on Print> Properties and set for glossy photo paper.
- Print the picture on the glossy label, then cut out along the hairline circle. (Do not remove the label backing at this point.)

Let's take a moment to go over the names of the parts of a watch:

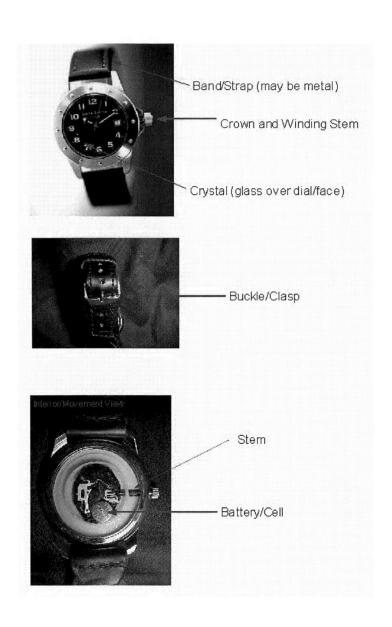

Band/Strap (may be metal)

Crown and Winding Stem

Crystal (glass over dial/face)

Buckle/Clasp

Interior/Movement View

Stem

Battery/Cell

Instructions for putting the dial on the watch

- Remove the back. If the watch has a snap back, hold the watch parallel to the ground at eye level, with the back up

and, using your loupe, find the notch or indentation

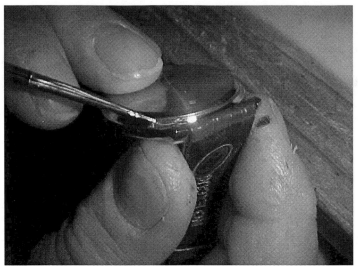

(sometimes identified by an arrow on the back)

 where the knife blade will go for the opening.

- Place a piece of plastic (baggie or plastic tape) over the case to protect it in case your knife should slip across the back and scratch it.

- Apply direct and even pressure with your watch knife in the groove or indentation between the back of the watch and the bezel

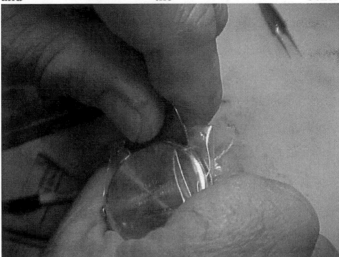

  until it is firmly seated between the two, then simply twist or rock the blade to open the back.

- To remove a screw-on back, using a spanner, fit the two top pins using the width adjustment with the thumbwheel

 and then
fit the third by turning the handle, just snug enough to
stay in place as you turn the caseback. (If you tighten
them too much, they can pop out when you turn the
tool.)

Once the back has been removed, there will be a few things
you will want to make note of. First is the position of the
back gasket, (it will be suspended around the caseback or it
has a place on the watch bezel where it goes). Make note of
where it goes. Next, note the movement ring.

www.watchfix.com   www.watchrepairbooks.com
www.watchrepairvideos.com   www.watchrepairseminars.com

You will notice that it has a cutout in which the stem goes.

Next we need to remove the stem from the watch. There are three methods of removing a stem from a watch. All employ the same basic technology, but in a slightly different way: Here are different types of detents/set levers you will commonly find on watches.

As you practice with more and more watches, you will easily find the detent yourself.

- Friction   detent/   set   lever

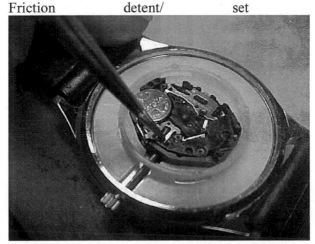

There are two types. There is the set-lever type that by pressing the indentation on it while gently pulling on the stem allows the stem to be removed.

- Button type in which you push a button that releases the stem as you pull on it.
- Screw detent/ set lever – this type of detent/set lever is more commonly used in mechanical watches and enables the stem to be removed by slightly loosening the screw, only until the stem easily comes out.

- Now remove the movement ring by gently lifting it with your tweezers.

- When the stem and movement ring have been removed from the watch, the dial and movement (they are attached to each other) are ready to be taken out by gently lifting it or by turning the watch case over and letting it fall into your hand.

- Once the movement and dial have been removed from the case, the stem and crown should be replaced back into the

movement. This will allow you to more easily line up the picture as you place it on the dial, as well as allow you to reset the hands perfectly.

Hand removal –

- First move the hands so that they are directly lined up over   each   other.

- Then take a piece of plastic (baggie or plastic wrap) and drape it over the hands and watch.
- Take your hand removers (bow or scissor type) and identify the two non-scratch pads at the bottom of the tool. On newer models, this will be fiberglass or rubber, on older models this will be leather. Make sure it is free of anything that may scratch the dial or stain it.
- With the hands aligned over each other, place the hand removers to straddle the hands, at a 90-degree

angle.   On   both

types of hand removers, there are pry-boards that fit underneath the hour hand. Make sure that when the hand remover is place firmly against the dial, the pry bar is under the hour hand.

- If you are using bow hand removers, simply press the sides of the bow in.

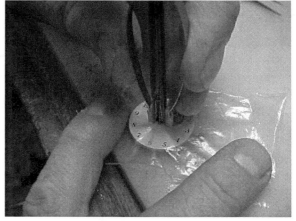

- This will cause the plunger in the center to hold the hands steady while the pry bar pulls the hands off the watch movement.
- In the case of scissor hand removers, once you have the pads   firmly   against   the   dial

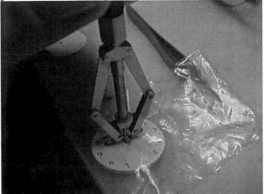

and the pry bar under the hour hand, simply slide the barrel down to remove   the   hands.

- Once the hands have been successfully removed, place them to one side to prepare for the next step.

Preparing the picture for the dial:

- You have your picture cut out and the center and 3:00 position marked on it

- Take your convocal punch, your picture dial and on a soft surface such as wood or plastic, place the dial, face

up, and place the punch over the center

- Tap it with a small bench hammer to punch out the hole for the center.

Once this is done, the picture is ready to be transferred to the dial.

- Peel   the   picture

                                           from
the covering.
- With the picture face up over the watch dial, line up the picture to the watch dial at the 3:00 markings, and then position the center hole you have punched over the post for the hands. Before you press the picture down completely, make sure the alignment is correct.
- Using the protective covering you have peeled off the back   to   protect   the

picture,   press
the picture down onto the dial, making sure that there are

no air bubbles causing the dial to be raised in some sections. (If there are air bubbles, the hands can rub along them and get caught on them and stop the watch.)

Putting the hands back on the watch.

- Place the hour hand at the 3:00

(if you are right-handed) or 9:00 (if you are left-handed) position.
- With the side of your pair of tweezers, press the hour hand onto the post from which you removed it.
- Now check the alignment so that it is pointing to the center of where the 3:00 or 9:00 position would be, making sure that it is also parallel to the dial.
- Place the minute hand pointing at the 12:00 position on top of the smaller post that is still protruding from the dial, and, as with the hour hand, press the minute hand down

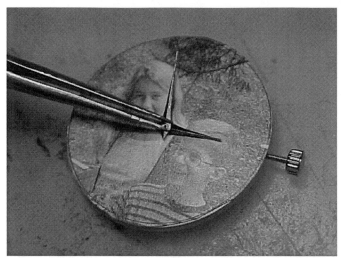

to secure it in place. Again, make sure the hand is parallel to the dial so that it will not drag or catch on the hour hand.

- On models that have a second hand, place the second hand on the sweep second pinion (the thinnest post that is still protruding from the dial), press it gently onto the pinion.

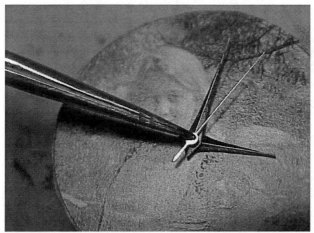

Align the second hand over the minute hand by pushing it gently with your tweezers to make sure there is clearance.

Checking the clearance of the hands all the way around the dial can be done one of two ways.

- One way is to manually turn the hands around while holding the dial at eye level to check that the hands clear, making any slight adjustments as may be necessary. Move the hands by pulling the stem out one notch, as if to set the hands and turn the crown.
- Another way is to use an impulse generator as can be found on a quartz watch timing machine, testing machine or Cyclotron,

 so that the hands spin around 24 hours to verify that the hands do not touch anywhere.

Now you are ready to place the movement back into the case.

* Remove the stem by manipulating the detent/set lever as previously   done

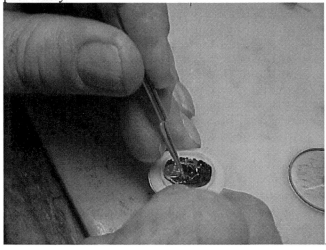

- Then with a bulb aspirator

or canned air

make sure there is no dust, lint, or foreign particles on the inside of the case or crystal, as well as the dial.
- Place the movement and dial back into the case, lining the stem of the movement towards the hole in the case for the stem.

- Place the stem back into the movement

- Before replacing the movement ring or back, check again the alignment of the hands and whether or not there is any dust or particles between the dial and the crystal.
- Once you are satisfied that these details are settled, place the movement ring back into the case.
- Take a swab of silicone and place a small amount on the hole where the stem goes into the watch

and all around the back where it will snap onto the case.

- Check to see if the back has a notch which would go over the stem

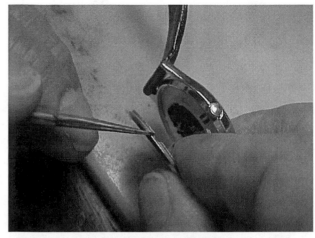

(it may not), line it up if it does, and put the back on with the case closer.

Now   You're   Done!

Marketing Your PictureWatch Business

Now that you have the skills to create your own Picture Watches, what do you do?

One of the really beautiful things about picture watches is that they really fit well with word of mouth advertising! Picture this – a grandmother wearing a PictureWatch of her grandchildren to church, synagogue, or senior activities center. It is the most natural thing for her to show off her grandkids to her friends. Each and every time she does, it is a powerful advertisement for you that money just can't buy. That's why we suggest one very effective way for you to get your picture watch business off the ground is to give a few away to some active, high profile people, for example, priest, minister, rabbi, local businessperson, the local high school football hero or cheerleader, to name a few. These people, without even being asked to do so in most cases, are only too happy to "tell 'em where they got it." And in the case of the football or cheerleader type, it is a great substitute for those expensive class rings.

These are some of the ways our dealers have marketed PictureWatches successfully:

- Fund Raisers
- Fraternal Organizations
- Company Logos
- Holidays
- Promotions in Conjunction with Glamour Photo Shops
- Schools

Fund Raisers - Here are just a few ideas of how PictureWatches can be effective fundraisers: Virtually every church or synagogue in America is looking for creative ways to raise funds. Sell them PictureWatches that say the name and/or logo of the organization and the level of contribution, such as "Diamond Contributor," "Gold Contributor," "Silver Contributor" for different levels of donations, along with their name. In the case of fund raising, often times they request a much higher quality watch. This equates to more profit for you.

Fraternal Organizations - Many of you already belong to the Elks, Eagles, AmVets, Masons, etc. These groups are always looking for unique presentations, other than trophies, awards, etc. A good technique is to give a complimentary watch to the head of the local organization. It's sure to be noticed by many, which will create demand.

Company Logos - Every year many small to medium sized companies spend thousands of dollars on promotional items and employee incentive programs, such as pens, letter openers, coffee mugs, etc. Your local Chamber of

www.watchfix.com
www.watchrepairvideos.com
www.watchrepairbooks.com
www.watchrepairseminars.com

414

Commerce can give you a list of the active businesses in your area to whom you can sell PictureWatches. Companies also may want to use PictureWatches as employee

incentives. You can send a letter to a business to let them know about the unique employee incentives and retirement gifts you can provide.

Holidays - Holidays open all types of opportunities for selling PictureWatches. Dials can be designed with hearts for Valentines day, Christmas decorations, menorahs or Star of David for Jewish holidays, names, greetings

(such as "We Love Grandma") along with photos.

Glamour Shops - Glamour Shops do "make-overs" for

women and then take a photograph. They are usually located in malls. Talk with the Manager/Owner about having them add a PictureWatch to their offerings.

.

STUDENT OF THE MONTH
What great public relations it would be for you to donate

one to each month's student. _____ Of course, other children and parents will see the PictureWatch, which creates demand. High school student's parents need an atlernative to a $500 palladium class ring.   There is an alternative!   PictureWatches. Giving one away to the Captain of the football team and Head Cheerleader can create even more demand.

Portability

Tremendous opportunities are available to you if you can "take the show on the road." Some examples of this are:
- **Church Bazars**
- **County Fairs**
- **Craft Events at Malls**
- **Local Artisan Shows**

To take advantage of this, you will need some kind of electrical source (if it is not available you can bring your own source – such as an "uniterruptable power supply" avilable through www.apcc.com), all the computer equipment listed previously, and a digital camera with some sort of backdrop to take the pictures against. If

you are at a big event, you may want to have a banner with the event name behind the subject.

If you are in a situation where you simply cannot actually make the PictureWatches at the location, you can still set up a booth or table, take the photos with the backdrop, complete the PictureWatches at your office or home and send them to the customer. If this is the case, be sure to collect the money when you take the picture and order.

Displays for PictureWatches

You can make a simple display for your picture watches like this:

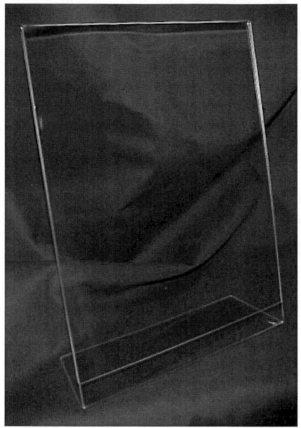

This is an 8 ½ " X 11" clear lucite flyer holder, available at most office supply stores.

Make up your own flyer for it, or use our template:

Available Exclusively at [Your Nam

Company Logo

Gandma's Favorite

Personal Mess

Whatever You

2-SD-087

ONLY
$79.

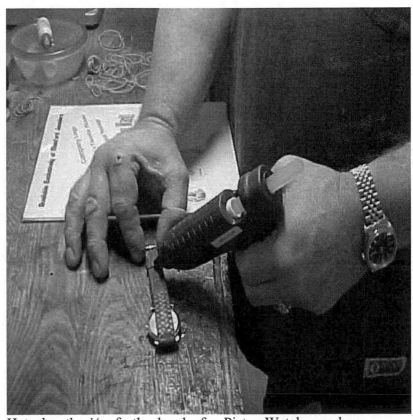

Hot glue the ½ of the band of a PictureWatch you have made.

Attach the watch to the lucite flyer holder.

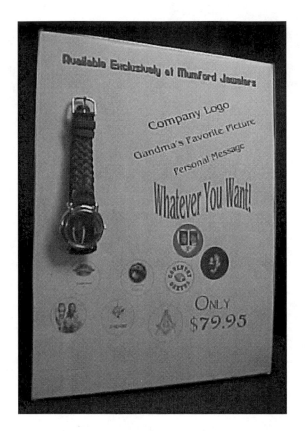

There is your display!

Here are some ads you can use:

These are just some of the possibilities for success with PictureWatches! If you find something that works for you, please let us know.

Here are some sample of picture watches YOU can do:

Epilogue – It's TIME to Make MORE Money

Back in the 1970s there was a literary phenomenon -- "browser's books". There was a _Browser's Book of Beginnings, Browser's Book of Gardening, Browser's Book of Cooking_, etc. If we have done our job well here, this book should become your "Browser's Book of Watch Repair".

Refer to it from time to time, brush up on the chapters, re-learn what you already know occasionally, and this book will serve you well as the tool it was intended to be.

Hopefully, by now you are beginning to learn to love watch repairs!

--Dan & Sheila Gendron

About the Authors

Dan Gendron comes from a long line of watchmakers, going back six generations to the 1840s in Canada. Dan's own training began at the age of 10, under the tutelage of his father, Henri Louis Gendron. Dan built up his family's watch repair business by directly contacting and delivering repairs to retail jewelers throughout New England. By the age of 28, Dan was proprietor of his own watch repair trade shop, and was the national repair center for several national chain jewelry stores.

In the last 30 years, Dan Gendron has become a highly respected, internationally known horologist specializing in the repair of high grade watches, and is especially known for his exceptional level of customer service.

Sheila Gendron works by Dan's side day in and day out, in a team effort to re-vitalize the watch repair service industry. Currently, the Gendrons offer classes in **Profitable Quartz Watch Repair** across the country as well as in-store consultations to retail jewelers, emphasizing the smooth running and profitability of a retail jewelry store watch repair department and basic watch repair techniques, as well as offering repair accounts to the trade.

Professional Affiliations

Founder and National Executive Director,
National Horological Institute
Society for Professional Watchmakers

Jewelers Vigilance Committee Member
Lifetime Polygon Member
Publisher of Watch Repair Times

www.watchfix.com   www.watchrepairbooks.com
www.watchrepairvideos.com   www.watchrepairseminars.com
430

Author of
The Video Series, A Course In Profits Through Service

Author of
I Hate Watches...or...How I Learned to Stop Hating Them
and Love the Profits

Dan Gendron Horology
Roswell, NM 88201
888-750-3330
www.watchfix.com

www.watchrepairseminars.com

www.watchrepairvideos.com

www.watchrepairbooks.com

www.watchfix.com
www.watchrepairvideos.com

www.watchrepairbooks.com
www.watchrepairseminars.com